D1544223

Mathematics for Christian Living Series

+ × = − ÷
Honest Heart
For what shall it profit a man, if he shall gain the whole world, and lose his own soul?
Full Measure

Mathematics for Christian Living Series

Exploring Arithmetic

Grade 3

Rod and Staff Publishers, Inc.

Hwy. 172, Crockett, Kentucky 41413

Telephone: (606) 522-4348

Acknowledgments

We are indebted to God for the vision of the need for a *Mathematics for Christian Living Series* and for His enabling grace. Charitable contributions from many churches have helped to cover the expenses for research and development.

This revision was written by Sisters Miriam Rudolph and Marla Martin. The brethren Marvin Eicher, Jerry Kreider, and Luke Sensenig served as editors. Sister Lois Myer drew the illustrations. The work was evaluated by a panel of reviewers and tested by teachers in the classroom. Much effort was devoted to the production of the book. We are grateful for all who helped to make this book possible.

—The Publishers

Printed in U.S.A.

ISBN 978-07399-0462-6

Catalog no. 13301.3

14 15 16 — 23 22 21 20 19 18 17

Table of Contents

1.	9	5	2	4	2	7	4
	+ 1	+ 3	+ 3	+ 5	+ 7	+ 0	+ 6
2.	5	3	4	3	5	2	6
	+ 4	+ 5	+ 2	+ 6	+ 2	+ 8	+ 2
3.	3	2	1	6	3	2	1
	+ 7	+ 5	+ 8	+ 3	+ 2	+ 6	+ 9
4.	7	7	4	8	2	4	7
	+ 1	+ 3	+ 3	+ 1	+ 4	+ 4	+ 2
5.	0	8	3	2	1	4	3
	+ 8	+ 2	+ 4	+ 2	+ 2	+ 1	+ 3
6.	5	2	6	4	5	3	0
	+ 5	+ 4	+ 1	+ 6	+ 1	+ 4	+ 0
7.	1	1	2	1	1	6	1
	+ 5	+ 4	+ 1	+ 3	+ 6	+ 4	+ 7

8. eleven fifty-six

9. ninety-nine thirteen

8.	11	56
9.	99	13

10. seventy-four forty-eight

11. twenty-five sixty-one

12. eighty seventeen

13. thirty-six sixty-seven

14. fourteen seventy-five

"The LORD on high is mightier than . . .
the mighty waves of the sea."

Psalm 93:4

1.	10 - 8	9 - 4	8 - 4	10 - 5	7 - 0	5 - 1	5 - 2
2.	6 - 3	8 - 2	5 - 3	8 - 7	3 - 2	10 - 9	3 - 1
3.	8 - 5	7 - 3	10 - 3	8 - 3	6 - 2	7 - 2	8 - 6
4.	6 - 4	9 - 8	7 - 6	5 - 4	4 - 2	7 - 1	7 - 4
5.	9 - 6	10 - 4	9 - 5	8 - 1	10 - 7	9 - 1	7 - 5
6.	10 - 1	3 - 3	10 - 4	9 - 0	9 - 9	9 - 3	10 - 7
7.	6 - 4	10 - 2	9 - 6	9 - 2	10 - 6	9 - 3	4 - 1

"He is . . . mighty in strength." Job 9:4

8. one hundred — two hundred eight

9. two hundred ninety-nine — two hundred fifty

10. two hundred nineteen — one hundred twenty

11. one hundred ninety-five — one hundred twelve

12. one hundred sixty-two — one hundred forty

13. two hundred twenty-six — two hundred ten

14. two hundred seventeen — two hundred six

15. one hundred eighty-one — two hundred nine

16. two hundred thirteen — one hundred eleven

17. one hundred seventy-one — two hundred two

18. one hundred forty-eight — one hundred one

19. two hundred fifteen — one hundred fifty

20. one hundred ninety-six — one hundred five

1.	6 + 4	9 - 3	3 + 5	5 + 2	9 - 5	3 + 7	8 - 2
2.	5 + 4	10 - 6	7 - 3	7 - 0	2 + 6	3 + 6	6 - 2
3.	10 - 3	3 - 2	9 - 2	5 + 3	8 - 1	2 + 5	10 - 9
4.	8 - 4	6 - 6	3 + 4	10 - 2	1 + 6	1 + 3	9 - 9
5.	9 - 7	6 + 3	10 - 3	10 - 5	9 - 1	6 - 4	4 + 5
6.	8 - 5	5 - 3	1 + 7	3 + 2	6 + 1	9 - 6	8 - 6
7.	6 - 1	7 - 4	6 - 5	8 - 3	6 - 3	7 - 6	5 - 4

"He is . . . mighty in strength." Job 9:4

8.  =

9.  =

10.  =

8.	4¢	
9.		
10.		
11.	53¢	20¢

11.	53 pennies =	20 pennies =
12.	98 pennies =	26 pennies =
13.	76 pennies =	67 pennies =
14.	62 pennies =	89 pennies =
15.	10 pennies =	35 pennies =
16.	19 pennies =	46 pennies =
17.	87 pennies =	29 pennies =
18.	43 pennies =	34 pennies =
19.	92 pennies =	78 pennies =
20.	64 pennies =	91 pennies =

1.	1	2	6	4	2	3	2
	3	3	2	2	5	1	7
	+ 4	+ 4	+ 2	+ 3	+ 3	+ 1	+ 1
2.	2	2	1	1	7	1	1
	2	4	6	4	1	2	3
	+ 5	+ 4	+ 2	+ 3	+ 1	+ 5	+ 6
3.	3	1	5	1	3	1	5
	2	1	1	2	3	5	0
	+ 5	+ 3	+ 4	+ 6	+ 4	+ 3	+ 3
4.	6	3	2	2	3	2	3
	1	1	6	4	4	5	2
	+ 3	+ 4	+ 1	+ 2	+ 2	+ 3	+ 4
5.	1	4	3	3	6	3	2
	2	4	3	2	0	4	4
	+ 7	+ 2	+ 2	+ 5	+ 4	+ 3	+ 3
6.	2	4	5	2	2	5	1
	5	3	2	0	2	1	8
	+ 2	+ 3	+ 3	+ 8	+ 4	+ 4	+ 1

"He is . . . mighty in strength." Job 9:4

7.  =

8.  =

9.  =

10. 95 pennies = 82 pennies =

11. 42 pennies = 68 pennies =

12. 37 pennies = 73 pennies =

13. 86 pennies = 24 pennies =

14. 28 pennies = 59 pennies =

15. 39 pennies = 85 pennies =

16. 18 pennies = 81 pennies =

17. 79 pennies = 97 pennies =

18. 14 pennies = 81 pennies =

19. 58 pennies = 93 pennies =

1.	5	12	9	11	9	11	12
	+ 7	− 8	+ 3	− 5	+ 2	− 8	− 4
2.	12	11	3	11	12	12	2
	− 3	− 9	+ 8	− 6	− 9	− 4	+ 9
3.	11	12	6	12	7	11	6
	− 3	− 9	+ 5	− 6	+ 5	− 7	+ 6
4.	7	12	11	12	4	11	11
	+ 4	− 4	− 8	− 7	+ 7	− 9	− 2
5.	11	8	8	12	11	4	7
	− 6	+ 3	+ 4	− 5	− 4	+ 8	+ 4
6.	9	12	11	8	11	12	12
	+ 3	− 8	− 6	+ 4	− 7	− 7	− 6
7.	5	3	11	12	4	4	12
	+ 6	+ 9	− 4	− 5	+ 8	+ 7	− 7

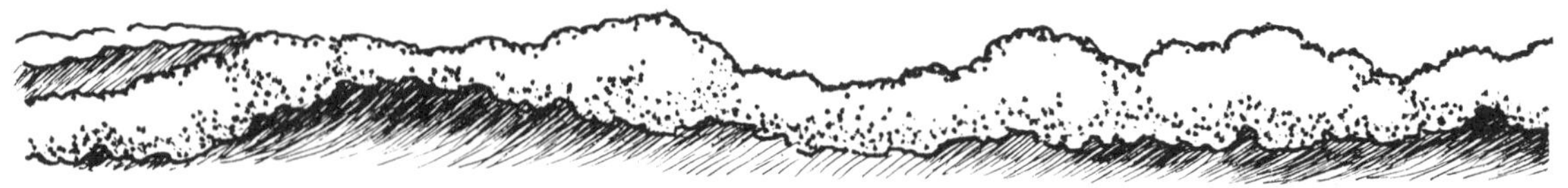

"He is . . . mighty in strength." Job 9:4

8.  =

9.  =

10. =

11.	7 dimes =	8 dimes =
12.	1 dime =	3 dimes =
13.	4 dimes =	2 dimes =
14.	3 dimes =	5 dimes =
15.	6 dimes =	4 dimes =
16.	5 dimes =	7 dimes =
17.	8 dimes =	6 dimes =
18.	7 dimes =	9 dimes =
19.	1 dime =	8 dimes =
20.	9 dimes =	2 dimes =

1.	13 − 7	4 + 8	7 + 4	13 − 5	13 − 4	3 + 8	13 − 9
2.	13 − 8	9 + 4	12 − 4	6 + 5	13 − 6	8 + 5	11 − 5
3.	13 − 9	9 + 2	12 − 3	11 − 3	8 + 3	9 + 3	13 − 7
4.	12 − 6	5 + 8	13 − 6	5 + 6	12 − 4	4 + 9	13 − 8
5.	8 + 4	7 + 6	3 + 9	12 − 5	12 − 8	12 − 9	12 − 7
6.	13 − 8	11 − 8	11 − 7	11 − 4	5 + 7	6 + 7	7 + 5
7.	13 − 5	7 + 6	13 − 4	2 + 9	13 − 4	5 + 8	13 − 5

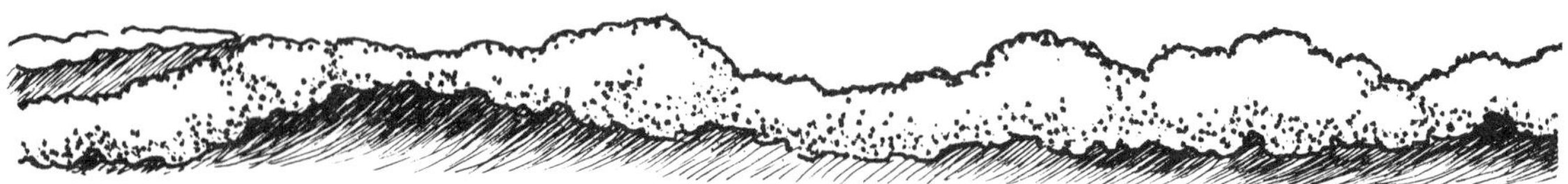

"He is . . . mighty in strength." Job 9:4

8.  =

9.  =

10.  =

11. 7 dimes = 6 dimes =

12. 5 dimes = 8 dimes =

13. 6 dimes = 7 dimes =

14. 4 dimes = 9 dimes =

15. 5 dimes = 8 dimes =

16. 3 dimes = 1 dime =

17. 4 dimes = 9 dimes =

18. 2 dimes = 3 dimes =

19. 3 dimes = 1 dime =

20. 1 dime = 2 dimes =

1.	9 + 4	14 − 6	12 − 8	14 − 5	8 + 6	12 − 9	14 − 7
2.	13 − 5	8 + 5	14 − 5	13 − 9	11 − 8	6 + 8	13 − 6
3.	8 + 6	12 − 8	9 + 4	7 + 7	14 − 5	12 − 6	5 + 9
4.	9 + 5	5 + 8	13 − 9	14 − 5	5 + 9	6 + 8	13 − 7
5.	12 − 3	9 + 5	14 − 6	14 − 7	11 − 4	14 − 7	11 − 6
6.	7 + 7	13 − 4	11 − 4	14 − 6	14 − 7	13 − 6	13 − 8
7.	7 + 6	8 + 4	14 − 8	14 − 9	14 − 8	5 + 7	6 + 7

"He is . . . mighty in strength." Job 9:4

8. There is one God. He made the earth in 6 days. He rested 1 day. How many days was that in all?

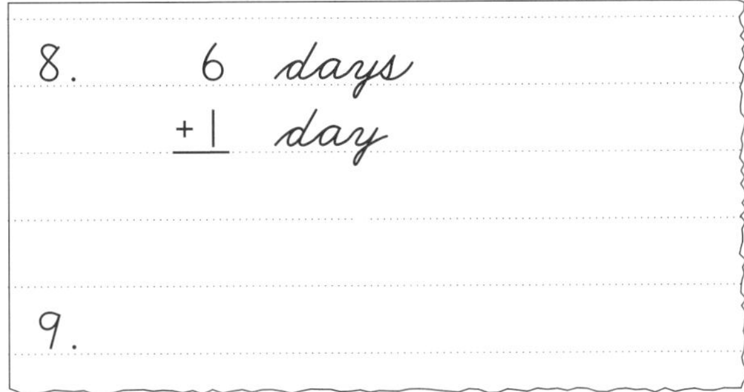

9. Jane looked in her pencil box. 3 pencils were blue. 5 pencils were green. How many pencils was that altogether?

10. 13 sheep grazed on a hill. Father took 6 of the sheep to the barn. How many sheep were left on the hill?

11. 14 gulls swooped above sea waves. 9 of the gulls flew away. How many gulls were left?

1.	$15 - 9$	$14 - 9$	$9 + 5$	$14 - 7$	$13 - 8$	$7 + 6$	$15 - 8$
2.	$14 - 9$	$14 - 8$	$15 - 8$	$8 + 5$	$12 - 7$	$13 - 6$	$5 + 9$
3.	$6 + 9$	$13 - 7$	$15 - 6$	$14 - 6$	$7 + 7$	$14 - 8$	$5 + 9$
4.	$15 - 9$	$9 + 6$	$8 + 6$	$12 - 6$	$6 + 8$	$14 - 6$	$15 - 6$
5.	$13 - 7$	$6 + 9$	$7 + 8$	$14 - 5$	$15 - 6$	$6 + 8$	$8 + 7$
6.	$7 + 8$	$15 - 9$	$8 + 7$	$8 + 6$	$14 - 5$	$15 - 6$	$7 + 8$
7.	$15 - 7$	$13 - 4$	$15 - 8$	$15 - 7$	$14 - 7$	$12 - 3$	$15 - 7$

"He is . . . mighty in strength." Job 9:4

8. Father read the Bible to his family. He read 7 verses about God's might. He read 4 verses about sea waves. How many verses was that in all?

9. 14 gulls rested on posts. 8 gulls flew away to the sand. How many gulls were left?

10. Carl's family watched seals at the zoo. A big seal ate 9 fish. A small seal ate 4 fish. How many fish was that in all?

11. Fay's family gathered 15 baskets of nuts. They gave 7 baskets to a rest home. How many baskets did they have left?

12. Mother canned 12 jars of plums. She gave 6 jars to Grandmother. How many jars did Mother have left?

1.	16 − 9	8 + 8	6 + 9	14 − 9	13 − 7	15 − 9	16 − 7
2.	14 − 8	13 − 8	8 + 7	8 + 8	16 − 9	15 − 6	15 − 9
3.	16 − 7	8 + 8	9 + 6	16 − 9	15 − 9	8 + 6	16 − 8
4.	5 + 9	14 − 7	7 + 8	7 + 9	16 − 7	16 − 8	5 + 9
5.	7 + 9	16 − 9	15 − 8	8 + 7	15 − 6	16 − 8	9 + 7
6.	16 − 7	7 + 8	15 − 8	13 − 6	9 + 7	8 + 8	15 − 7
7.	9 + 7	15 − 7	9 + 6	7 + 9	6 + 9	14 − 6	7 + 9

"He is . . . mighty in strength." Job 9:4

8.  =

9.  =

10.  =

11. 1 nickel = 5 nickels =

12. 6 nickels = 10 nickels =

13. 2 nickels = 4 nickels =

14. 7 nickels = 9 nickels =

15. 5 nickels = 3 nickels =

16. 10 nickels = 8 nickels =

17. 4 nickels = 2 nickels =

18. 9 nickels = 7 nickels =

19. 3 nickels = 1 nickel =

20. 8 nickels = 6 nickels =

10

1.	18 − 9	15 − 6	9 + 8	14 − 9	8 + 9	14 − 5	18 − 9
2.	14 − 8	18 − 9	17 − 8	16 − 9	7 + 9	9 + 6	16 − 7
3.	18 − 9	15 − 9	9 + 7	16 − 9	17 − 8	16 − 7	7 + 8
4.	15 − 8	17 − 9	16 − 8	8 + 9	9 + 7	9 + 9	15 − 7
5.	17 − 9	14 − 7	8 + 8	9 + 8	16 − 8	14 − 6	9 + 9
6.	6 + 9	7 + 9	17 − 8	16 − 9	16 − 8	8 + 9	17 − 9
7.	7 + 9	8 + 7	16 − 8	16 − 9	17 − 8	17 − 9	9 + 8

"He is . . . mighty in strength." Job 9:4

8.  (6 nickels) =

9.  (4 nickels) =

10.  (5 nickels) =

11. 10 nickels = 11 nickels =

12. 12 nickels = 9 nickels =

13. 8 nickels = 13 nickels =

14. 1 nickel = 7 nickels =

15. 6 nickels = 2 nickels =

16. 3 nickels = 5 nickels =

17. 4 nickels = 6 nickels =

18. 7 nickels = 3 nickels =

19. 2 nickels = 9 nickels =

20. 5 nickels = 8 nickels =

1.	18 − 9	9 + 8	14 − 8	8 + 8	15 − 9	8 + 9	14 − 5
2.	16 − 9	9 + 6	17 − 9	6 + 8	16 − 7	9 + 7	6 + 9
3.	7 + 8	14 − 7	8 + 6	16 − 8	7 + 9	17 − 8	7 + 7
4.	6 + 9	9 + 5	14 − 6	15 − 8	5 + 9	15 − 7	8 + 7
5.	5 + 9	7 + 8	15 − 8	17 − 9	15 − 7	8 + 6	6 + 8
6.	15 − 6	9 + 8	7 + 9	16 − 7	17 − 8	14 − 7	9 + 7
7.	8 + 9	17 − 8	18 − 9	8 + 8	16 − 9	15 − 6	9 + 9

"He gathereth the waters of the sea." Psalm 33:7

8. three hundred — three hundred two

9. five hundred ninety-nine — four hundred sixty

10. five hundred thirteen — three hundred four

11. four hundred sixteen — four hundred fifty

12. five hundred fourteen — three hundred six

13. five hundred seventeen — four hundred eighty

---

14. Gulls made 17 nests on rocks by the sea. 9 nests had eggs in them. How many nests did not have eggs?

15. 18 apples were in a lunch. Glen's family ate 9 of them. The rest they took to Grandfather. How many apples did they take to him?

1.	$9 + 9$	$17 - 9$	$2 + 9$	$8 + 8$	$16 - 8$	$9 + 7$	$8 + 6$
2.	$9 + 7$	$6 + 5$	$11 - 3$	$9 + 9$	$13 - 8$	$15 - 6$	$14 - 7$
3.	$12 - 7$	$18 - 9$	$9 + 8$	$14 - 6$	$5 + 9$	$7 + 9$	$13 - 5$
4.	$15 - 7$	$8 + 9$	$13 - 4$	$14 - 9$	$13 - 6$	$14 - 5$	$11 - 6$
5.	$12 - 6$	$9 + 5$	$15 - 8$	$9 + 6$	$13 - 7$	$9 + 4$	$12 - 8$
6.	$8 + 7$	$16 - 9$	$6 + 8$	$11 - 5$	$13 - 9$	$7 + 6$	$13 - 7$
7.	$17 - 8$	$15 - 9$	$7 + 8$	$7 + 7$	$16 - 7$	$14 - 8$	$6 + 9$

"He gathereth the waters of the sea." Psalm 33:7

8.  =

9.  =

10.  =

11. 1 nickel = 6 dimes =

12. 9 nickels = 12 pennies =

13. 1 dime = 13 nickels =

14. 4 dimes = 13 pennies =

15. 3 nickels = 7 dimes =

16. 7 nickels = 14 pennies =

17. 2 dimes = 10 nickels =

18. 3 dimes = 3 nickels =

19. 5 nickels = 8 dimes =

1.	17	12	18	12	15	13	12
	- 9	- 3	- 9	- 4	- 9	- 9	- 5
2.	13	12	12	15	15	14	15
	- 7	- 9	- 7	- 8	- 9	- 9	- 7
3.	14	13	14	13	12	14	11
	- 5	- 5	- 6	- 4	- 8	- 8	- 4
4.	11	12	13	13	11	11	16
	- 8	- 6	- 6	- 8	- 6	- 5	- 8
5.	16	11	16	17	16	17	16
	- 9	- 7	- 7	- 8	- 9	- 9	- 8
6.	15	16	17	15	13	17	15
	- 9	- 7	- 9	- 6	- 7	- 8	- 7
7.	13	14	18	11	15	15	14
	- 9	- 7	- 9	- 2	- 7	- 8	- 6

"He gathereth the waters of the sea." Psalm 33:7

8. six hundred | nine hundred twenty

9. nine hundred ninety | eight hundred five

10. nine hundred eighteen | six hundred eighteen

11. nine hundred three | six hundred seven

12. six hundred seventeen | six hundred nineteen

13. six hundred eight | eight hundred six

14. nine hundred sixteen | seven hundred sixteen

15. seven hundred six | three hundred nine

16. eight hundred sixteen | eight hundred nineteen

17. nine hundred forty | eight hundred sixty

18. eight hundred sixty-nine | nine hundred seventy

19. nine hundred fifty | six hundred twenty

20. seven hundred forty-nine | nine hundred sixty

1.	9 + 8	15 − 9	17 − 9	14 − 7	13 − 8	7 + 8	8 + 4
2.	14 − 8	8 + 9	7 + 5	6 + 9	14 − 9	15 − 8	16 − 8
3.	8 + 7	11 − 3	16 − 9	6 + 8	7 + 6	13 − 7	12 − 3
4.	15 − 7	9 + 6	11 − 2	12 − 6	8 + 5	5 + 9	13 − 6
5.	18 − 9	4 + 9	15 − 6	9 + 7	14 − 5	13 − 5	14 − 6
6.	5 + 8	17 − 8	15 − 7	12 − 4	13 − 4	7 + 9	16 − 7
7.	8 + 6	12 − 5	6 + 7	9 + 9	9 + 4	11 − 4	9 + 5

"He gathereth the waters of the sea." Psalm 33:7

8.  =

9.  =

10.  =

11. 10 nickels = 15 pennies =

12. 9 nickels = 7 nickels =

13. 12 nickels = 6 nickels =

14. 9 dimes = 65 pennies =

15. 8 nickels = 4 dimes =

16. 13 nickels = 90 pennies =

17. 3 dimes = 6 dimes =

18. 35 pennies = 45 pennies =

19. 3 nickels = 5 dimes =

1.	75 + 2	86 + 3	68 − 5	95 + 4	59 − 4	37 − 3
2.	67 − 2	95 + 3	89 − 3	58 − 6	73 + 5	39 − 7
3.	39 − 5	58 − 3	94 + 5	69 − 6	83 + 6	73 + 4
4.	37 − 5	72 + 6	56 − 4	88 − 2	94 + 4	69 − 4
5.	92 + 5	67 − 4	72 + 4	39 − 2	82 + 3	59 − 8
6.	88 − 4	97 − 6	92 + 7	67 + 2	96 − 5	86 − 2
7.	58 − 7	83 + 2	37 − 0	74 + 2	66 − 3	94 + 3

"He gathereth the waters of the sea." Psalm 33:7

8. God does not sleep, but people do. Keith slept 9 hours on Sunday night. On Monday night he slept 8 hours. How many hours was that altogether?

9. 18 stickers were in a book. The children stuck 9 of them on Bible memory charts. How many stickers were left in the book?

10. Lightning flashed in the south and west. Mark saw 15 flashes. 9 of the flashes were in the south. How many flashes were in the west?

11. 17 gulls stood on rocks. 9 of them swooped away. How many gulls stayed on the rocks?

12. Mighty waves pounded on 15 rocks. 8 of the rocks were swept away to sea. How many rocks were not swept away?

1.	73 + 95	65 + 94	84 + 53	83 + 73	95 + 73	92 + 43
2.	65 + 42	94 + 82	84 + 65	42 + 85	44 + 64	93 + 86
3.	96 + 63	86 + 82	72 + 84	73 + 64	53 + 82	72 + 96
4.	81 + 95	33 + 74	81 + 46	54 + 95	82 + 97	71 + 37
5.	56 + 53	93 + 75	83 + 76	64 + 83	42 + 94	72 + 56
6.	82 + 27	81 + 95	76 + 93	83 + 86	95 + 84	47 + 62
7.	85 + 83	65 + 44	72 + 75	75 + 84	36 + 92	64 + 72

"He gathereth the waters of the sea." Psalm 33:7

8. 

=

9. 

=

10. 

=

11. 2 quarters = 4 quarters =

12. 3 quarters = 1 quarter =

---

13. Ray picked 56 apples from a large tree and 43 apples from a small tree. How many apples did he pick from both trees?

14. 68 pears filled a basket. 46 of them were ripe. How many pears were not ripe?

15. 16 butterflies sailed over the garden. 7 of them flitted away. How many butterflies were left?

1.	87 - 64	99 - 53	87 - 33	98 - 95	99 - 47	99 - 28
2.	64 - 40	95 - 92	99 - 34	77 - 63	76 - 46	95 - 74
3.	88 - 17	77 - 25	79 - 76	76 - 22	88 - 42	76 - 53
4.	84 - 63	93 - 63	68 - 54	88 - 23	88 - 85	59 - 35
5.	74 - 22	69 - 61	96 - 21	89 - 66	78 - 36	65 - 22
6.	68 - 66	89 - 54	49 - 47	78 - 43	83 - 33	87 - 27
7.	88 - 45	96 - 54	66 - 43	89 - 14	58 - 50	87 - 35

"He gathereth the waters of the sea." Psalm 33:7

8. 

=

9. 

=

10. 

=

11. 3 quarters = 1 quarter =

12. 4 quarters = 2 quarters =

13. 5 + 7 − 8 = 7 + 9 − 7 =

14.

13. 5 + 7 − 8 = 7 + 9 − 7 =

14. 7 + 8 − 9 = 8 + 7 − 7 =

15. 9 + 6 − 7 = 7 + 4 − 5 =

16. 6 + 8 − 5 = 6 + 5 − 7 =

1.	97 - 22	52 + 95	87 - 85	83 + 84	83 + 95	73 + 93
2.	94 + 75	96 - 93	43 + 64	82 + 93	99 - 86	94 + 63
3.	76 + 33	94 + 92	86 - 64	96 - 65	92 + 74	92 + 86
4.	93 + 82	65 + 42	79 - 76	76 + 93	82 + 75	88 - 75
5.	64 - 33	95 - 73	92 + 94	32 + 77	65 + 93	77 - 34
6.	74 + 93	56 - 54	64 + 83	99 - 24	95 - 52	74 + 84
7.	98 - 74	89 - 33	93 + 56	86 - 62	98 - 42	85 + 64

"He gathereth the waters of the sea." Psalm 33:7

8. $8 + 9 - 8 =$ $4 + 9 - 8 =$

9. $6 + 8 - 7 =$ $4 + 7 - 4 =$

10. $4 + 8 - 7 =$ $8 + 8 - 7 =$

11. $6 + 9 - 7 =$ $5 + 7 - 4 =$

12. $9 + 6 - 8 =$ $3 + 9 - 5 =$

13. $6 + 7 - 5 =$ $4 + 8 - 4 =$

14. God made each shell of the sea. Carl found 45 shells one day and 63 shells the next. How many shells did he find on both days?

15. 3 gulls flew to a cliff.
4 gulls flew to a tree.
8 gulls flew to a ship.
How many gulls flew in all?

1.	186 - 92	168 - 95	148 - 83	168 - 74	158 - 76
2.	159 - 96	108 - 37	189 - 97	166 - 74	179 - 94
3.	177 - 83	139 - 74	157 - 84	145 - 63	159 - 65
4.	118 - 55	177 - 85	149 - 78	167 - 82	187 - 95
5.	149 - 52	139 - 59	137 - 66	169 - 77	149 - 56
6.	177 - 84	168 - 83	179 - 81	149 - 56	179 - 94
7.	137 - 40	126 - 55	128 - 48	158 - 65	178 - 86

"He gathereth the waters of the sea." Psalm 33:7

8. four hundred five hundred forty

9. nine hundred ninety six hundred seventy

10. four hundred nineteen five hundred seventeen

11. six hundred seven seven hundred eight

12. eight hundred seven seven hundred six

13. seven hundred fifteen nine hundred fourteen

14. Grandfather gave 98¢ to Lester for his birthday. Lester gave 35¢ to the church and saved the rest. How many cents did he save?

15. A mother gull sat on her nest of eggs in the rain. It rained 4 hours in the morning, 3 hours in the afternoon, and 6 hours in the night. How many hours did the gull sit in the rain?

1.						
5	5	3	4	5	2	3
3	4	3	4	2	7	4
+ 4	+ 8	+ 8	+ 7	+ 9	+ 9	+ 8

2.						
2	3	4	3	3	6	6
4	6	5	5	2	3	2
+ 9	+ 9	+ 7	+ 7	+ 9	+ 8	+ 4

3.						
2	2	6	5	5	4	1
3	6	3	3	3	3	5
+ 8	+ 8	+ 8	+ 4	+ 7	+ 7	+ 5

4.						
8	5	3	3	7	3	4
1	2	5	6	2	5	2
+ 2	+ 7	+ 7	+ 3	+ 8	+ 8	+ 7

5.						
4	2	2	6	4	5	1
4	5	2	3	5	3	2
+ 9	+ 7	+ 8	+ 4	+ 8	+ 8	+ 8

6.						
5	4	3	2	1	1	6
4	4	6	5	3	7	2
+ 2	+ 8	+ 8	+ 6	+ 8	+ 6	+ 9

"He gathereth the waters of the sea." Psalm 33:7

7. 

=

8. 

=

9. =

10. 1 quarter = 10 nickels =

11. 3 dimes = 6 dimes =

12. 13 nickels = 3 quarters =

13. 12 nickels = 6 nickels =

14. 2 quarters = 5 nickels =

15. 8 dimes = 4 nickels =

16. 8 nickels = 4 dimes =

17. 2 dimes = 11 nickels =

1.	15 + 9	79 + 7	67 + 8	99 + 9	78 + 8	18 + 6
2.	38 + 9	86 + 8	29 + 5	79 + 6	47 + 9	19 + 8
3.	85 + 7	54 + 8	35 + 8	44 + 7	73 + 9	64 + 9
4.	18 + 9	49 + 7	78 + 7	28 + 6	87 + 7	39 + 8
5.	69 + 4	79 + 3	47 + 4	38 + 5	58 + 4	87 + 5
6.	49 + 8	17 + 9	66 + 9	89 + 5	77 + 8	58 + 9
7.	59 + 8	78 + 7	85 + 9	69 + 6	19 + 7	48 + 9

"The LORD . . . placed the sand." Jeremiah 5:22

8. $18 - 9 + 5 =$ $15 - 9 + 6 =$

9. $16 - 9 + 8 =$ $15 - 6 + 4 =$

10. $17 - 9 + 5 =$ $16 - 7 + 6 =$

11. $15 - 7 + 4 =$ $15 - 8 + 7 =$

12. $17 - 8 + 7 =$ $16 - 8 + 9 =$

13. A gull egg was ready to hatch. The chick in the shell pecked for 18 hours. It kept pecking for 6 hours more. Then the egg cracked open. How many hours did the chick peck altogether?

14. A mother gull and her chicks made 78 tracks in the wet sand. 52 tracks were small. How many were large?

1.	77 + 29	66 + 28	39 + 15	17 + 86	23 + 68	58 + 27
2.	32 + 59	26 + 77	17 + 37	58 + 36	59 + 47	47 + 38
3.	68 + 39	27 + 49	29 + 33	37 + 69	57 + 38	46 + 37
4.	49 + 58	55 + 28	68 + 27	69 + 37	37 + 25	18 + 58
5.	47 + 28	34 + 27	23 + 29	56 + 49	37 + 55	37 + 68
6.	58 + 34	38 + 67	34 + 18	27 + 34	38 + 37	88 + 17
7.	46 + 49	69 + 18	49 + 39	37 + 37	58 + 29	59 + 36

"The LORD . . . placed the sand." Jeremiah 5:22

8.   

9.   

8. 2:00 3:00 6:00

9.

10. one thousand

11. one thousand, nine hundred ninety-nine

12. one thousand, four hundred fifty-eight

13. one thousand, seven hundred sixty-three

14. one thousand, three hundred twenty-nine

15. one thousand, eight hundred fifty

16. one thousand, five hundred forty

1.	79 + 7	87 + 7	66 + 8	59 + 9	65 + 9	86 + 8
2.	88 + 9	95 + 8	73 + 9	62 + 9	78 + 9	98 + 2
3.	77 + 18	54 + 29	37 + 49	62 + 38	73 + 28	28 + 55
4.	28 + 64	37 + 25	15 + 36	36 + 59	56 + 24	28 + 59
5.	35 + 57	69 + 18	33 + 47	67 + 28	24 + 27	24 + 38
6.	58 + 37	57 + 26	26 + 75	34 + 66	49 + 37	29 + 54
7.	69 + 28	41 + 59	49 + 38	29 + 42	59 + 23	68 + 35

"The LORD . . . placed the sand." Jeremiah 5:22

8. one thousand, two hundred ninety-seven

9. one thousand, four hundred seventy-six

10. one thousand, six hundred fifty-five

11. one thousand, eight hundred thirty-four

12. one thousand, three hundred eighty-three

13. one thousand, five hundred sixty-two

14. one thousand, seven hundred forty-one

15. one thousand, nine hundred twenty

16.   

17.   

1.	126 + 34	876 + 18	333 + 58	566 + 17	615 + 67
2.	626 + 56	555 + 28	747 + 18	868 + 26	114 + 46
3.	253 + 37	865 + 19	344 + 47	225 + 59	529 + 66
4.	537 + 58	237 + 47	738 + 27	859 + 25	247 + 43
5.	632 + 58	542 + 39	659 + 17	758 + 39	846 + 29
6.	838 + 37	769 + 28	627 + 49	538 + 43	625 + 65
7.	328 + 62	538 + 55	714 + 38	317 + 73	524 + 69

"The LORD . . . placed the sand." Jeremiah 5:22

8. =

9. 

=

10. 

=

11.

2 quarters	6 dimes
+ 4 nickels	+ 7 nickels

11.	50¢	60¢
	+ 20¢	+ 35¢
12.		

12.

11 nickels	3 quarters
+ 34 pennies	+ 23 pennies

13.

8 dimes	1 quarter
+ 3 nickels	+ 10 nickels

1.	779 + 216	287 + 392	566 + 419	458 + 216	297 + 471
2.	225 + 358	272 + 585	356 + 639	365 + 483	524 + 459
3.	496 + 183	667 + 328	458 + 527	476 + 292	345 + 329
4.	581 + 276	357 + 226	247 + 748	419 + 564	484 + 364
5.	625 + 358	355 + 592	536 + 258	244 + 238	286 + 653
6.	317 + 678	158 + 738	375 + 464	438 + 557	367 + 529
7.	594 + 353	357 + 626	427 + 367	654 + 285	337 + 145

"The LORD . . . placed the sand." Jeremiah 5:22

8.   =

9.   =

10.   =

11. 5 nickels + 74 pennies

3 quarters + 2 dimes

12. 1 quarter + 7 dimes

6 dimes + 7 nickels

13. 3 dimes + 13 nickels

10 nickels + 36 pennies

14. 2 quarters + 5 nickels

9 nickels + 43 pennies

1.	176	159	185	148	167
	- 92	- 94	- 95	- 83	- 83
2.	169	114	133	129	167
	- 92	- 52	- 40	- 37	- 70
3.	179	164	157	107	158
	- 82	- 70	- 92	- 43	- 81
4.	158	188	155	145	136
	- 75	- 96	- 62	- 83	- 83
5.	149	139	156	165	147
	- 96	- 75	- 91	- 71	- 64
6.	96	93	67	74	76
	- 24	- 42	- 32	- 23	- 55
7.	95	98	88	87	87
	- 74	- 36	- 53	- 25	- 15

"The LORD . . . placed the sand." Jeremiah 5:22

8. Every book in the Bible is from God. The first part of the Bible has 39 books. The last part of the Bible has 27 books. How many books are in both parts?

9. Mother canned 36 jars of jam and 24 jars of pears. What was the sum of jars that Mother canned?

10. Jane saved 58¢ one week and 39¢ the next. What is the sum of cents that she saved?

11. Gulls dropped 38 clams down on rocks. The shells of 24 clams shattered. How many clams had shells that did not shatter?

12. God calls all the stars by their names. Fay knows only 10 names for stars. Lee tells her 4 more names. What sum of names is that?

1.	55 - 9	87 - 9	76 - 9	98 - 9	43 - 7	71 - 3
2.	62 - 3	30 - 7	72 - 8	20 - 3	77 - 9	42 - 6
3.	97 - 8	75 - 8	86 - 8	54 - 8	65 - 7	94 - 7
4.	22 - 5	71 - 7	32 - 9	61 - 2	93 - 6	64 - 6
5.	63 - 5	70 - 6	41 - 9	62 - 4	73 - 9	40 - 8
6.	94 - 5	72 - 7	30 - 4	71 - 8	96 - 7	54 - 9
7.	71 - 6	93 - 4	72 - 9	31 - 5	53 - 8	95 - 6

"The LORD . . . placed the sand." Jeremiah 5:22

8. one thousand, two hundred seventy-nine

9. two thousand, four hundred eight

10. one thousand, five hundred eighty-six

11. two thousand, seven hundred four

12. one thousand, nine hundred two

13.   

14 Dean helps in the barn for 60 minutes each day. How many hours does he help in the barn each day? *Write the rule.*

15. Mark's family drove 1 hour to get to church. How many minutes did it take them to get to church? *Write the rule.*

14. 60 *minutes* = 1 *hour*

15. 1 *hour* = 60 *minutes*

1.	93 - 79	95 - 59	96 - 78	82 - 68	84 - 48	85 - 67
2.	96 - 37	90 - 87	76 - 49	64 - 29	84 - 35	64 - 36
3.	90 - 16	93 - 66	42 - 14	70 - 54	82 - 73	82 - 25
4.	50 - 33	92 - 47	92 - 36	66 - 27	95 - 27	74 - 25
5.	81 - 36	41 - 24	51 - 12	81 - 25	73 - 24	84 - 16
6.	96 - 39	95 - 86	63 - 47	91 - 63	84 - 57	91 - 17
7.	53 - 25	93 - 44	73 - 38	75 - 48	52 - 49	85 - 26

"The LORD . . . placed the sand." Jeremiah 5:22

8.  =

9.  =

10.

3 quarters	2 quarters
+ 4 nickels	+ 4 dimes

11.

11 nickels	5 dimes
+ 34 pennies	+ 9 nickels

---

12. A minister preached for 60 minutes. How many hours did he preach? *Write the rule.*

13. A gull followed a ship for 1 hour and then flew to the sand to rest. How many minutes did the gull follow the ship? *Write the rule.*

1.	97 − 29	84 − 47	82 − 35	93 − 77	85 − 47	97 − 48
2.	90 − 53	86 − 18	85 − 36	70 − 32	82 − 66	93 − 46
3.	78 − 29	75 − 57	70 − 44	62 − 27	94 − 35	93 − 65
4.	91 − 56	61 − 35	64 − 46	67 − 18	82 − 54	83 − 24
5.	96 − 49	50 − 32	96 − 67	71 − 34	74 − 29	53 − 49
6.	44 − 26	85 − 38	92 − 88	63 − 18	66 − 29	85 − 56
7.	92 − 23	85 − 49	91 − 33	87 − 29	94 − 58	81 − 12

"The LORD . . . placed the sand." Jeremiah 5:22

8.  

9.   

10. 17 - 8 + 9 = 15 - 8 + 9 =

11. 13 - 7 + 8 = 10 - 6 + 8 =

12. 17 - 9 + 2 = 14 - 9 + 3 =

13. On a bookshelf there are 5 books about birds, 4 books about trees, and 9 books about people who trusted in God. What is the sum of books on the shelf?

14. In a basket there are sixteen apples with stems and twenty apples with no stems. What is the sum of apples in the basket?

30

1.	584 - 75	735 - 17	395 - 59	693 - 39	996 - 29
2.	884 - 67	662 - 53	990 - 44	777 - 49	497 - 58
3.	366 - 47	594 - 69	675 - 37	845 - 16	743 - 35
4.	978 - 49	677 - 29	967 - 38	666 - 18	380 - 61
5.	732 - 24	854 - 25	664 - 26	580 - 55	355 - 36
6.	496 - 57	786 - 58	985 - 39	658 - 49	870 - 53
7.	985 - 18	680 - 26	384 - 48	744 - 26	573 - 64

"The LORD . . . placed the sand." Jeremiah 5:22

8. 

9.   

10. two thousand, one hundred ninety

11. two thousand, seven hundred eight

12. one thousand, two hundred six

13. two thousand, six hundred eighty

14. two thousand, three hundred four

15. one thousand, five hundred two

16. two thousand, four hundred seventy

---

17. Chester saved 85 stamps. Lester saved 63 stamps. What was the difference in the number of stamps that the boys saved?

31

1.	86 - 47	90 - 37	74 - 57	96 - 68	74 - 29	84 - 26
2.	96 - 48	94 - 76	75 - 69	54 - 29	70 - 44	76 - 47
3.	82 - 29	75 - 36	85 - 57	65 - 48	97 - 39	83 - 38
4.	86 - 68	85 - 37	43 - 18	94 - 88	85 - 56	65 - 39
5.	90 - 55	88 - 59	90 - 26	96 - 49	97 - 19	84 - 25
6.	64 - 8	98 - 9	82 - 4	83 - 5	97 - 8	65 - 9
7.	37 - 8	44 - 9	55 - 8	73 - 9	67 - 8	80 - 2

8. 1 quarter
+ 12 nickels

4 dimes
+ 9 nickels

9. 5 nickels
+ 68 pennies

2 quarters
+ 7 nickels

10. 5 + 8 − 6 =   18 − 9 + 6 =

11. 8 + 6 − 8 =   17 − 9 + 8 =

12. 5 + 9 − 9 =   16 − 8 + 7 =

13. 6 + 7 − 9 =   15 − 7 + 8 =

14. 4 + 7 − 9 =

"The LORD on high is mightier than . . .
the mighty waves of the sea."
Psalm 93:4

1.	96 - 79	79 - 34	50 - 47	96 - 76	95 - 46	94 - 36
2.	88 - 43	85 - 68	85 - 49	99 - 43	94 - 29	97 - 73
3.	87 - 29	86 - 37	85 - 65	42 - 39	79 - 55	57 - 39
4.	86 - 62	93 - 28	88 - 32	90 - 54	96 - 78	68 - 44
5.	97 - 68	99 - 46	74 - 48	80 - 32	88 - 26	97 - 24
6.	88 - 35	86 - 57	86 - 13	99 - 37	95 - 47	63 - 37
7.	77 - 32	94 - 77	99 - 79	51 - 48	97 - 39	90 - 41

"Thou rulest the raging of the sea." Psalm 89:9

8. 

9.  

10.   

11. 68 pears were yellow. 46 pears were green. What was the difference in the number of yellow and green pears?

12. Carl has 89¢. Roy has 32¢. What is the difference in the number of cents that the boys have?

13. A flock of gulls flew 446 miles one day and 334 miles the next. What was the sum of miles that the gulls flew?

1.	76 - 50	97 - 68	95 - 63	96 - 49	67 - 59	98 - 38
2.	75 - 47	75 - 39	99 - 42	87 - 22	94 - 87	99 - 65
3.	97 - 58	97 - 64	66 - 51	77 - 49	77 - 53	90 - 74
4.	96 - 67	94 - 34	94 - 58	85 - 56	86 - 26	83 - 47
5.	81 - 65	66 - 42	66 - 38	77 - 62	86 - 53	88 - 49
6.	89 - 55	73 - 66	98 - 33	89 - 32	64 - 28	54 - 26
7.	88 - 59	69 - 43	85 - 38	84 - 52	87 - 27	56 - 48

"Thou rulest the raging of the sea." Psalm 89:9

8.  

9.   

10.	17 − 8 + 7 =	7 + 9 − 8 =
11.	8 + 9 − 8 =	6 + 9 − 8 =
12.	15 − 8 + 9 =	8 + 8 − 8 =
13.	7 + 8 − 6 =	8 + 6 − 7 =

14. Kenneth said his Bible memory again and again for $\frac{1}{2}$ hour. How many minutes did he say his Bible memory? *Write the rule.*

15. Fred worked 30 minutes to make a neat arithmetic paper. What part of an hour did Fred work? *Write the rule.*

34

1.	377 - 29	878 - 36	790 - 36	499 - 49	686 - 49
2.	869 - 27	395 - 47	878 - 74	590 - 67	974 - 56
3.	795 - 70	588 - 12	697 - 58	698 - 66	874 - 17
4.	599 - 23	768 - 43	893 - 36	689 - 57	676 - 37
5.	695 - 36	389 - 68	986 - 68	582 - 59	869 - 65
6.	398 - 77	684 - 25	675 - 38	498 - 48	782 - 28
7.	473 - 44	795 - 39	765 - 65	784 - 28	468 - 39

"Thou rulest the raging of the sea." Psalm 89:9

8.

1 quarter + 7 dimes	13 nickels + 34 pennies

9.

9 nickels + 2 dimes	4 dimes + 11 nickels

10.

2 quarters + 49 pennies	3 quarters + 4 nickels

11.

8 nickels + 3 dimes	2 quarters + 4 nickels

12.

13. Keith and Lester sang for 30 minutes. What part of an hour did they sing? *Write the rule.*

14. Janet scrubbed windows for $\frac{1}{2}$ hour. How many minutes did she scrub? *Write the rule.*

35

1.	368 + 329	459 + 125	746 + 227	234 + 228	249 + 347
2.	137 + 459	329 + 349	536 + 349	364 + 629	459 + 238
3.	337 + 358	127 + 335	637 + 336	345 + 239	327 + 467
4.	278 + 516	259 + 734	529 + 356	219 + 459	428 + 267
5.	838 - 647	818 - 545	439 - 357	769 - 283	627 - 357
6.	369 - 175	778 - 394	703 - 683	859 - 475	457 - 263
7.	935 - 665	848 - 362	256 - 174	646 - 373	786 - 595

"Thou rulest the raging of the sea." Psalm 89:9

8. 57 gulls rode up and down on the mighty waves of the sea. 43 gulls flew over the waves. What was the difference in the number of gulls?

9. Father picked 68 peppers and sold one dozen of them. How many peppers did he have left?

10. Mother froze 37 boxes of white corn and one dozen boxes of yellow corn. What was the difference in the number of boxes?

11. Lois pressed 76 leaves. Joy pressed 34 leaves. What was the difference in the number of leaves that the girls pressed?

12. Milton and his big brother can sing 38 songs from *Life Songs*. They can sing 99 songs from the *Christian Hymnal*. What is the sum of songs that the boys can sing from both books?

1.	975 − 780	959 − 592	917 − 352	959 − 673	988 − 490
2.	879 − 381	719 − 235	967 − 294	419 − 246	869 − 674
3.	729 − 534	537 − 253	935 − 372	649 − 277	856 − 360
4.	948 − 452	738 − 366	824 − 261	426 − 142	638 − 443
5.	756 − 176	528 − 355	856 − 183	678 − 194	767 − 481
6.	679 − 393	878 − 592	856 − 291	848 − 481	949 − 369
7.	949 − 582	569 − 474	958 − 672	958 − 393	959 − 461

"Thou rulest the raging of the sea." Psalm 89:9

8. 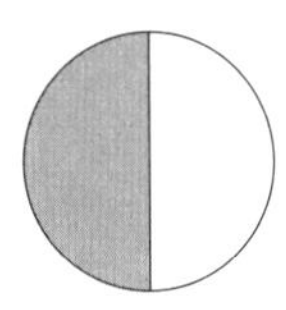 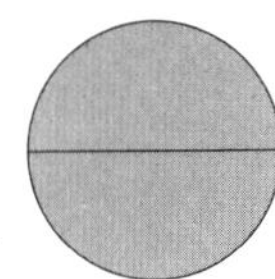 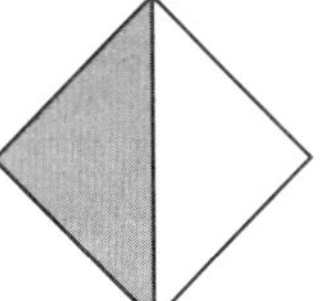 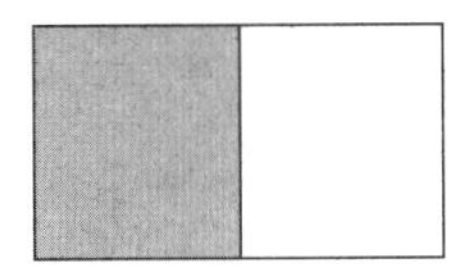

9. 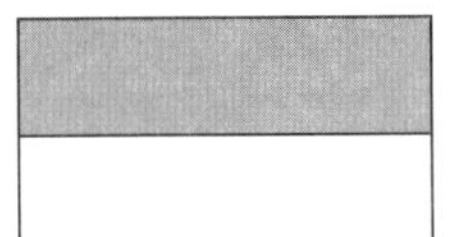 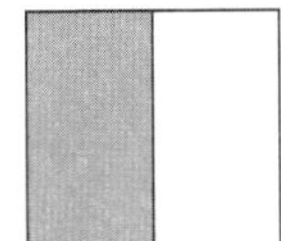 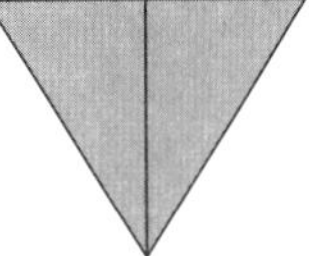 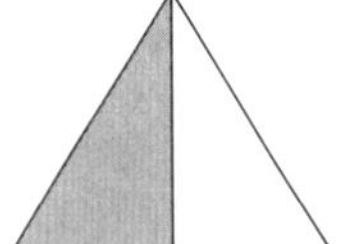

8. $\frac{1}{2}$ $\frac{2}{2}$ = 1 *whole* $\frac{1}{2}$ $\frac{1}{2}$

9.

10. two thousand, ninety-three

11. two thousand, eighty-seven

12. two thousand, seventy-nine

13. one thousand, sixty-two

14. two thousand, fifty-four

15. one thousand, forty-six

16. two thousand, thirty-eight

1.	986 - 679	659 - 293	898 - 679	785 - 538	909 - 642
2.	864 - 645	749 - 693	869 - 383	857 - 590	676 - 429
3.	984 - 237	659 - 574	587 - 368	748 - 382	895 - 588
4.	848 - 763	890 - 143	978 - 492	537 - 481	973 - 754
5.	985 - 747	757 - 439	947 - 452	865 - 537	996 - 857
6.	858 - 363	946 - 628	770 - 532	845 - 706	974 - 646
7.	690 - 566	879 - 585	685 - 595	967 - 673	782 - 658

"Thou rulest the raging of the sea." Psalm 89:9

8. 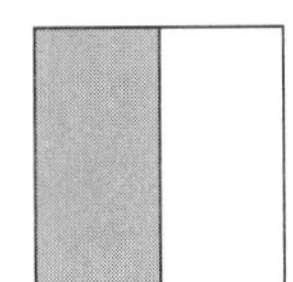 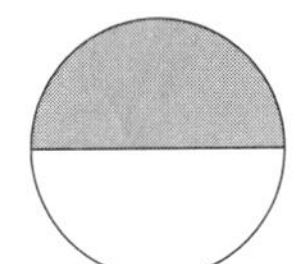 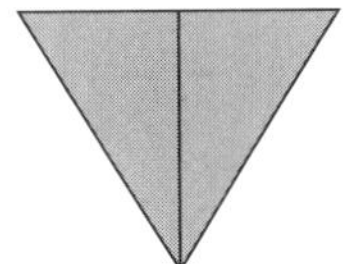 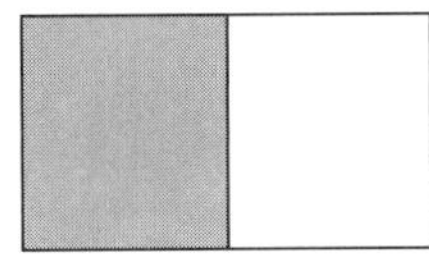

9. 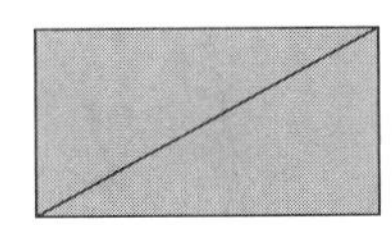 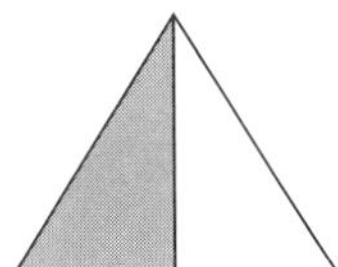 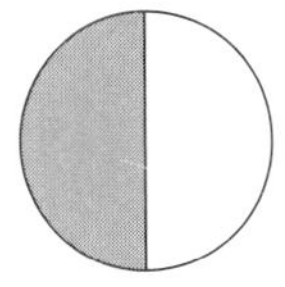 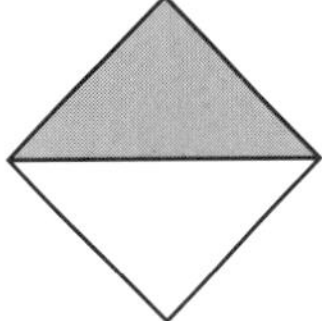

10. 17 - 9 + 7 = 15 - 8 + 7 =

11. 18 - 9 + 4 = 13 - 4 + 3 =

12. 16 - 7 + 5 = 11 - 5 + 9 =

13. 13 - 5 + 6 = 16 - 8 + 5 =

14. 17 - 8 + 4 = 16 - 9 + 7 =

15. 14 - 5 + 8 = 12 - 4 + 9 =

16. Henry's hens laid 9 eggs one day and $\frac{1}{2}$ dozen eggs the next day. What was the sum of eggs that the hens laid?

38

1.	905 - 26	506 - 49	205 - 69	803 - 89	604 - 76
2.	807 - 18	604 - 37	607 - 58	705 - 77	903 - 98
3.	904 - 99	704 - 76	606 - 57	603 - 36	808 - 19
4.	802 - 86	504 - 65	903 - 15	503 - 64	803 - 87
5.	705 - 26	507 - 39	705 - 47	607 - 68	407 - 29
6.	506 - 38	708 - 29	608 - 69	707 - 49	406 - 28
7.	505 - 48	906 - 27	802 - 88	204 - 68	605 - 77

"Thou rulest the raging of the sea." Psalm 89:9

8.  =

9.  =

10.  =

11.

12 nickels	2 quarters
+ 27 pennies	+ 7 nickels

12.

3 quarters	1 quarter
+ 4 nickels	+ 7 dimes

13. Chester helped to husk corn for 1 hour. How many minutes did he help? *Write the rule.*

14. Martha's family drove $\frac{1}{2}$ hour to get to a prayer meeting. How many minutes did they drive? *Write the rule.*

39

1.	905 - 269	907 - 659	704 - 399	808 - 479	703 - 467
2.	905 - 329	906 - 759	906 - 447	905 - 537	904 - 265
3.	805 - 658	804 - 228	704 - 336	805 - 346	807 - 168
4.	806 - 558	804 - 168	907 - 578	903 - 598	605 - 369
5.	704 - 227	606 - 457	603 - 126	705 - 556	903 - 129
6.	908 - 689	702 - 666	701 - 248	902 - 355	806 - 377
7.	907 - 478	801 - 254	802 - 349	901 - 865	807 - 588

"Thou rulest the raging of the sea." Psalm 89:9

8.  

9. one thousand, seventy-two

10. two thousand, thirty-nine

11. one thousand, ninety-three

12. two thousand, twenty-seven

13. two thousand, eighty-five

14. two thousand, forty-six

15. one thousand, sixty-four

16. one thousand, fifty-eight

---

17. 17 chicks hid in a box. $\frac{1}{2}$ dozen other chicks hid under their mother's wing. What was the sum of chicks that hid?

1.	903 − 285	902 − 453	807 − 739	902 − 745	803 − 274
2.	903 − 374	705 − 237	907 − 628	806 − 549	802 − 184
3.	905 − 579	803 − 646	806 − 738	801 − 352	603 − 247
4.	701 − 345	705 − 448	808 − 529	604 − 136	704 − 378
5.	608 − 79	906 − 59	707 − 68	504 − 99	807 − 59
6.	806 − 58	503 − 98	706 − 67	905 − 58	608 − 79
7.	605 − 36	705 − 47	804 − 27	704 − 46	604 − 35

"Thou rulest the raging of the sea." Psalm 89:9

8. 

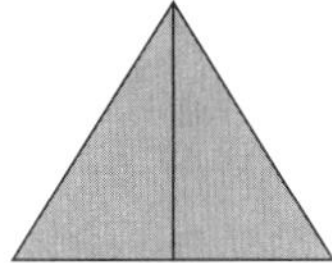 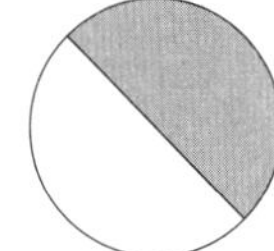 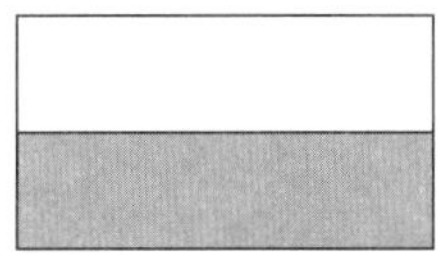 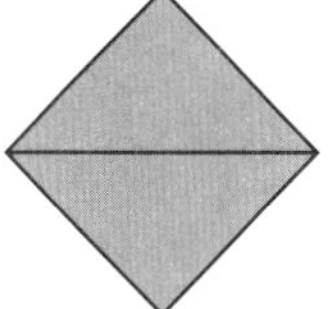

9.

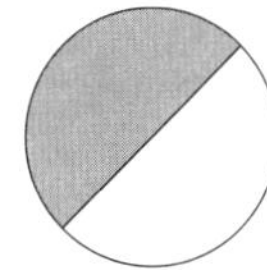 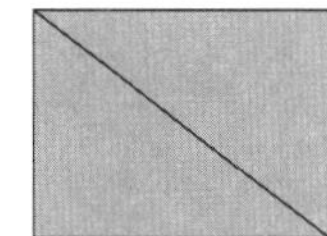 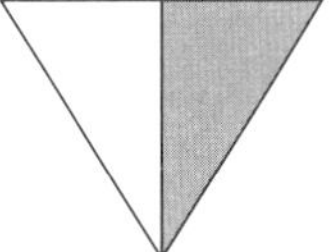 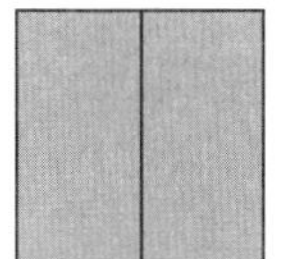

10. The Bible says that Noah lived for 950 years. Adam lived for 930 years. What was the difference in the number of years that these men lived?

11. Mother had 23 eggs. She sold $\frac{1}{2}$ dozen of them. How many eggs did she have left?

12. 33 gulls ate from the sand. 67 gulls swooped down to eat. What was the sum of the gulls?

1.	0 × 1	1 × 1	2 × 1	3 × 1	4 × 1	5 × 1	6 × 1
2.	7 × 1	8 × 1	9 × 1	10 × 1	11 × 1	12 × 1	
3.	7 × 1	3 × 1	1 × 1	0 × 1	1 × 1	3 × 1	7 × 1
4.	5 × 1	8 × 1	12 × 1	2 × 1	4 × 1	6 × 1	10 × 1
5.	9 × 1	11 × 1	0 × 1	10 × 1	1 × 1	11 × 1	12 × 1
6.	12 × 1	11 × 1	1 × 1	10 × 1	0 × 1	11 × 1	9 × 1
7.	10 × 1	6 × 1	4 × 1	2 × 1	12 × 1	8 × 1	5 × 1

"God said, Let the waters bring forth." Genesis 1:20

8. 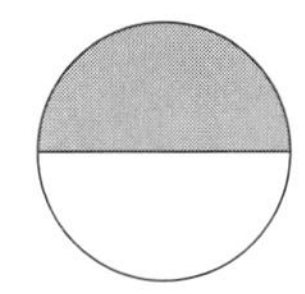 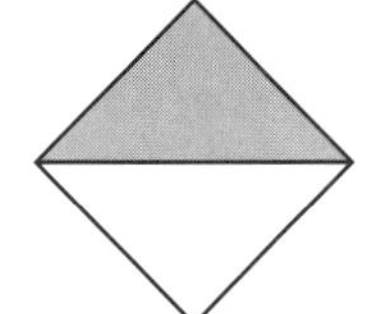 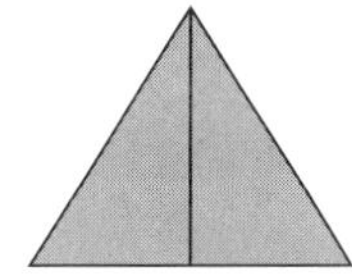 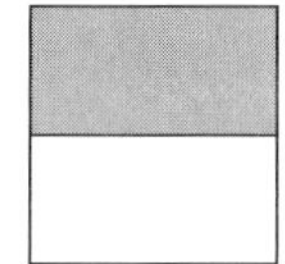

9. 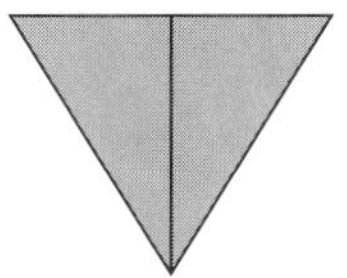 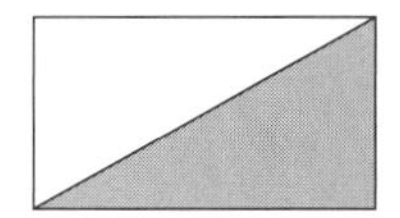 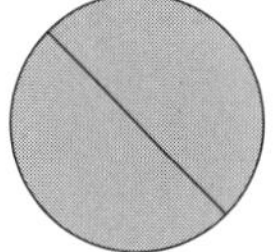 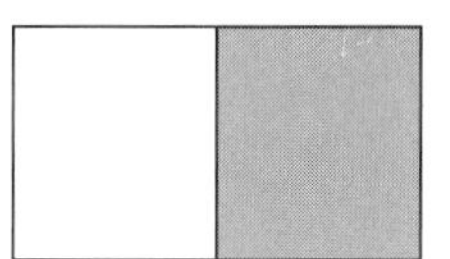

10.	8 + 7 − 6 =	13 − 8 + 9 =
11.	17 − 9 + 6 =	7 + 9 − 8 =
12.	8 + 9 − 9 =	18 − 9 + 5 =
13.	15 − 6 + 5 =	8 + 8 − 7 =
14.	7 + 7 − 8 =	5 + 6 − 8 =
15.	13 − 8 + 7 =	15 − 9 + 6 =
16.	4 + 8 − 9 =	5 + 8 − 7 =
17.	16 − 7 + 6 =	14 − 7 + 8 =

1.

9	1	8	6	7	2	6
× 1	× 1	× 1	× 1	× 1	× 1	× 1

2.

5	10	4	11	3	12	0
× 1	× 1	× 1	× 1	× 1	× 1	× 1

3.

6	2	7	0	8	1	9
× 1	× 1	× 1	× 1	× 1	× 1	× 1

4.

0	12	3	11	4	10	5
× 1	× 1	× 1	× 1	× 1	× 1	× 1

5.

962	948	605	946	805
- 447	- 782	- 356	- 652	- 428

6.

504	657	603	439	807
- 366	- 575	- 276	- 357	- 669

7.

906	867	407	659	883
- 529	- 573	- 158	- 493	- 368

"God said, Let the waters bring forth." Genesis 1:20

8.

2 quarters	3 quarters
+ 7 nickels	+ 23 pennies

9.

8 nickels	6 dimes
+ 2 dimes	+ 6 nickels

10. God covers the heavens with clouds. Rose saw 32 clouds that looked like sheep. 17 clouds looked like boats. What was the difference in the number of clouds?

11. A mighty wave swept 55 shells from the sand. 28 shells had snails in them. How many shells did not have snails?

12. Fred counted 46 waves that splashed on sand and 87 that splashed on rocks. What sum of waves did he count?

43

1.	0	1	2	3	4	5	6
	× 2	× 2	× 2	× 2	× 2	× 2	× 2
2.	7	8	9	10	11	12	
	× 2	× 2	× 2	× 2	× 2	× 2	
3.	4	9	0	7	2	11	9
	× 2	× 2	× 2	× 2	× 2	× 2	× 2
4.	1	5	10	3	6	8	12
	× 2	× 2	× 2	× 2	× 2	× 2	× 2
5.	12	8	6	3	10	5	1
	× 2	× 2	× 2	× 2	× 2	× 2	× 2
6.	9	11	2	7	0	9	4
	× 2	× 2	× 2	× 2	× 2	× 2	× 2
7.	8	11	12	10	12	11	8
	× 2	× 2	× 2	× 2	× 2	× 2	× 2

"God said, Let the waters bring forth." Genesis 1:20

8. 

9.   

10. two thousand, seventy-five

11. one thousand, sixty-eight

12. two thousand, ninety-four

13. two thousand, forty-nine

14. one thousand, eighty-six

---

15. Fay's family hiked in the woods for 60 minutes. How many hours did they hike? *Write the rule.*

16. Carl sat in the dentist's chair for 30 minutes. What part of an hour did he sit there? *Write the rule.*

1. 9×2 4×2 11×2 0×2 11×2 4×2 9×2

2. 8×2 6×2 10×2 9×2 3×2 12×2 7×2

3. 6×2 8×2 3×2 9×2 10×2 7×2 12×2

4. 5×2 11×2 2×2 0×2 12×2 8×2 1×2

5. 12×2 0×2 2×2 11×2 5×2 1×2 8×2

6. 7×2 5×2 1×2 6×2 9×2 12×2 8×2

7. 5×2 7×2 8×2 12×2 9×2 6×2 1×2

"God said, Let the waters bring forth." Genesis 1:20

8.  

9.   

10. Father read the Bible for 60 minutes. How many hours did he read? *Write the rule.*

11. Grandfather could not find his cane. For 30 minutes Jay helped to hunt for it. What part of an hour did Jay help? *Write the rule.*

12. $\begin{array}{r} 407 \\ -\ 278 \\ \hline \end{array}$ $\quad \begin{array}{r} 704 \\ -\ 266 \\ \hline \end{array}$ $\quad \begin{array}{r} 706 \\ -\ 288 \\ \hline \end{array}$ $\quad \begin{array}{r} 508 \\ -\ 359 \\ \hline \end{array}$ $\quad \begin{array}{r} 606 \\ -\ 339 \\ \hline \end{array}$

13. $\begin{array}{r} 805 \\ -\ 387 \\ \hline \end{array}$ $\quad \begin{array}{r} 802 \\ -\ 364 \\ \hline \end{array}$ $\quad \begin{array}{r} 506 \\ -\ 377 \\ \hline \end{array}$ $\quad \begin{array}{r} 905 \\ -\ 638 \\ \hline \end{array}$ $\quad \begin{array}{r} 807 \\ -\ 658 \\ \hline \end{array}$

1. $\begin{array}{r} 5 \\ \times 2 \\ \hline \end{array}$ $\begin{array}{r} 1 \\ \times 2 \\ \hline \end{array}$ $\begin{array}{r} 4 \\ \times 2 \\ \hline \end{array}$ $\begin{array}{r} 0 \\ \times 2 \\ \hline \end{array}$ $\begin{array}{r} 3 \\ \times 2 \\ \hline \end{array}$ $\begin{array}{r} 9 \\ \times 2 \\ \hline \end{array}$ $\begin{array}{r} 12 \\ \times 2 \\ \hline \end{array}$

2. $\begin{array}{r} 3 \\ \times 2 \\ \hline \end{array}$ $\begin{array}{r} 0 \\ \times 2 \\ \hline \end{array}$ $\begin{array}{r} 4 \\ \times 2 \\ \hline \end{array}$ $\begin{array}{r} 1 \\ \times 2 \\ \hline \end{array}$ $\begin{array}{r} 5 \\ \times 2 \\ \hline \end{array}$ $\begin{array}{r} 12 \\ \times 2 \\ \hline \end{array}$ $\begin{array}{r} 9 \\ \times 2 \\ \hline \end{array}$

3. $\begin{array}{r} 10 \\ \times 2 \\ \hline \end{array}$ $\begin{array}{r} 7 \\ \times 2 \\ \hline \end{array}$ $\begin{array}{r} 2 \\ \times 2 \\ \hline \end{array}$ $\begin{array}{r} 11 \\ \times 2 \\ \hline \end{array}$ $\begin{array}{r} 8 \\ \times 2 \\ \hline \end{array}$ $\begin{array}{r} 12 \\ \times 2 \\ \hline \end{array}$ $\begin{array}{r} 6 \\ \times 2 \\ \hline \end{array}$

4. $\begin{array}{r} 7 \\ \times 2 \\ \hline \end{array}$ $\begin{array}{r} 10 \\ \times 2 \\ \hline \end{array}$ $\begin{array}{r} 6 \\ \times 2 \\ \hline \end{array}$ $\begin{array}{r} 12 \\ \times 2 \\ \hline \end{array}$ $\begin{array}{r} 8 \\ \times 2 \\ \hline \end{array}$ $\begin{array}{r} 11 \\ \times 2 \\ \hline \end{array}$ $\begin{array}{r} 2 \\ \times 2 \\ \hline \end{array}$

5. $\begin{array}{r} 57 \\ +\ 69 \\ \hline \end{array}$ $\begin{array}{r} 77 \\ +\ 97 \\ \hline \end{array}$ $\begin{array}{r} 57 \\ +\ 88 \\ \hline \end{array}$ $\begin{array}{r} 66 \\ +\ 99 \\ \hline \end{array}$ $\begin{array}{r} 46 \\ +\ 78 \\ \hline \end{array}$ $\begin{array}{r} 38 \\ +\ 99 \\ \hline \end{array}$

6. $\begin{array}{r} 39 \\ +\ 85 \\ \hline \end{array}$ $\begin{array}{r} 67 \\ +\ 98 \\ \hline \end{array}$ $\begin{array}{r} 46 \\ +\ 99 \\ \hline \end{array}$ $\begin{array}{r} 85 \\ +\ 89 \\ \hline \end{array}$ $\begin{array}{r} 48 \\ +\ 78 \\ \hline \end{array}$ $\begin{array}{r} 58 \\ +\ 79 \\ \hline \end{array}$

7. $\begin{array}{r} 66 \\ +\ 96 \\ \hline \end{array}$ $\begin{array}{r} 55 \\ +\ 88 \\ \hline \end{array}$ $\begin{array}{r} 66 \\ +\ 97 \\ \hline \end{array}$ $\begin{array}{r} 73 \\ +\ 89 \\ \hline \end{array}$ $\begin{array}{r} 86 \\ +\ 57 \\ \hline \end{array}$ $\begin{array}{r} 68 \\ +\ 95 \\ \hline \end{array}$

"God said, Let the waters bring forth." Genesis 1:20

8. 2 quarters + 4 dimes | 12 nickels + 39 pennies

9. 3 quarters + 4 nickels | 3 dimes + 9 nickels

10. 11 nickels + 10 pennies | 1 quarter + 10 nickels

11. 4 dimes + 7 nickels | 3 quarters + 20 pennies

12.

13.

14. Mother cooked $\frac{1}{2}$ dozen crabs and froze 8. What sum of crabs did Mother have?

1.	7×2	3×1	1×2	11×2	0×1	6×2	8×2
2.	12×2	5×1	3×2	0×2	5×2	8×2	12×1
3.	4×2	12×2	9×2	1×2	10×2	10×2	2×2
4.	10×2	1×2	9×2	12×2	8×1	4×1	10×2
5.	10×1	0×2	6×1	5×1	12×2	11×2	12×1
6.	1×1	11×2	2×1	3×1	7×2	6×2	11×2
7.	8×2	7×1	9×2	9×1	8×2	7×1	9×2

"God said, Let the waters bring forth." Genesis 1:20

8.

803	805	903	608	804
- 479	- 537	- 456	- 339	- 479

9. God can count all the grains of sand by the sea. We cannot count all of them. Roy counted 63 grains. Lee counted 48. How many more grains did Roy count than Lee?

10. God made many kinds of crabs. Carl listed 48 kinds. Mae listed 35 kinds. How many more kinds did Carl list than Mae?

11. Dean and Fred went on a crab hunt. Dean caught 47 crabs. Fred caught 33. How many more crabs did Dean catch than Fred?

12. Mighty waves swished crabs from the sand. 53 crabs were blue and 36 were green. How many more crabs were blue than green?

47

1. $\begin{array}{r}0\\ \times 3\\ \hline\end{array}$ $\begin{array}{r}1\\ \times 3\\ \hline\end{array}$ $\begin{array}{r}2\\ \times 3\\ \hline\end{array}$ $\begin{array}{r}3\\ \times 3\\ \hline\end{array}$ $\begin{array}{r}4\\ \times 3\\ \hline\end{array}$ $\begin{array}{r}5\\ \times 3\\ \hline\end{array}$ $\begin{array}{r}6\\ \times 3\\ \hline\end{array}$

2. $\begin{array}{r}7\\ \times 3\\ \hline\end{array}$ $\begin{array}{r}8\\ \times 3\\ \hline\end{array}$ $\begin{array}{r}9\\ \times 3\\ \hline\end{array}$ $\begin{array}{r}10\\ \times 3\\ \hline\end{array}$ $\begin{array}{r}11\\ \times 3\\ \hline\end{array}$ $\begin{array}{r}12\\ \times 3\\ \hline\end{array}$

3. $\begin{array}{r}1\\ \times 3\\ \hline\end{array}$ $\begin{array}{r}9\\ \times 3\\ \hline\end{array}$ $\begin{array}{r}10\\ \times 3\\ \hline\end{array}$ $\begin{array}{r}2\\ \times 3\\ \hline\end{array}$ $\begin{array}{r}8\\ \times 3\\ \hline\end{array}$ $\begin{array}{r}7\\ \times 3\\ \hline\end{array}$ $\begin{array}{r}4\\ \times 3\\ \hline\end{array}$

4. $\begin{array}{r}7\\ \times 3\\ \hline\end{array}$ $\begin{array}{r}11\\ \times 3\\ \hline\end{array}$ $\begin{array}{r}0\\ \times 3\\ \hline\end{array}$ $\begin{array}{r}7\\ \times 3\\ \hline\end{array}$ $\begin{array}{r}6\\ \times 3\\ \hline\end{array}$ $\begin{array}{r}12\\ \times 3\\ \hline\end{array}$ $\begin{array}{r}6\\ \times 3\\ \hline\end{array}$

5. $\begin{array}{r}9\\ \times 3\\ \hline\end{array}$ $\begin{array}{r}3\\ \times 3\\ \hline\end{array}$ $\begin{array}{r}5\\ \times 3\\ \hline\end{array}$ $\begin{array}{r}12\\ \times 3\\ \hline\end{array}$ $\begin{array}{r}4\\ \times 3\\ \hline\end{array}$ $\begin{array}{r}3\\ \times 3\\ \hline\end{array}$ $\begin{array}{r}8\\ \times 3\\ \hline\end{array}$

6. $\begin{array}{r}8\\ \times 3\\ \hline\end{array}$ $\begin{array}{r}3\\ \times 3\\ \hline\end{array}$ $\begin{array}{r}4\\ \times 3\\ \hline\end{array}$ $\begin{array}{r}12\\ \times 3\\ \hline\end{array}$ $\begin{array}{r}5\\ \times 3\\ \hline\end{array}$ $\begin{array}{r}3\\ \times 3\\ \hline\end{array}$ $\begin{array}{r}9\\ \times 3\\ \hline\end{array}$

7. $\begin{array}{r}6\\ \times 3\\ \hline\end{array}$ $\begin{array}{r}12\\ \times 3\\ \hline\end{array}$ $\begin{array}{r}6\\ \times 3\\ \hline\end{array}$ $\begin{array}{r}7\\ \times 3\\ \hline\end{array}$ $\begin{array}{r}0\\ \times 3\\ \hline\end{array}$ $\begin{array}{r}11\\ \times 3\\ \hline\end{array}$ $\begin{array}{r}7\\ \times 3\\ \hline\end{array}$

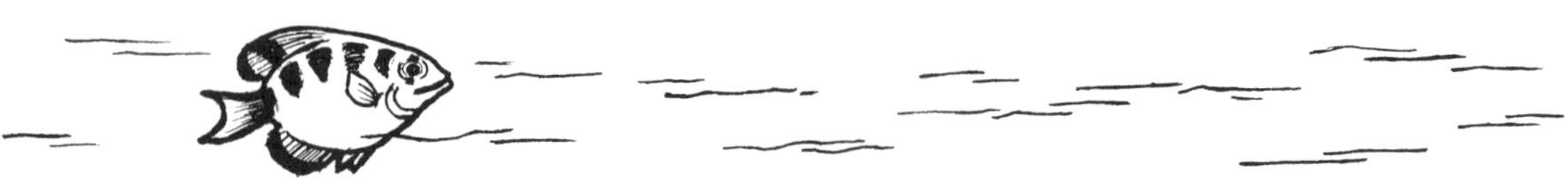

"The fishes of the sea shall declare unto thee . . ." Job 12:8

8. 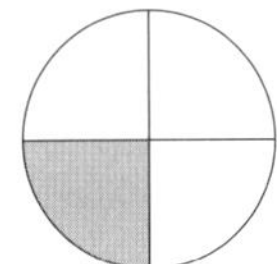  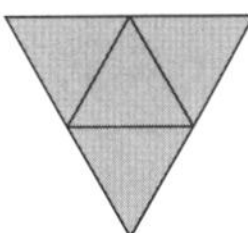 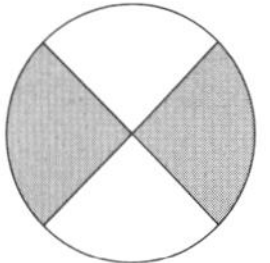

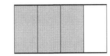

9. 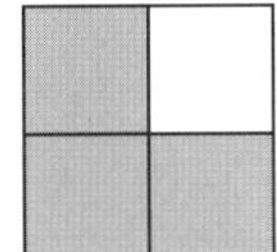 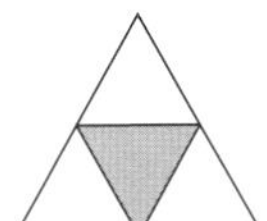 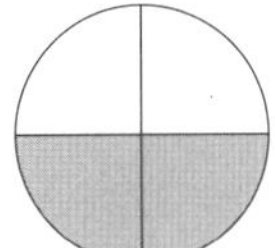 

8. $\frac{1}{4}$ $\frac{3}{4}$ $\frac{4}{4}$ = 1 *whole* $\frac{2}{4}$

9.

10. one thousand, forty-three

11. two thousand, thirty-four

12. one thousand, fifty-eight

13. two thousand, eighty-five

14. one thousand, sixty-seven

15.

25	61	53	23	52	33
40	33	43	54	33	42
+ 83	+ 72	+ 62	+ 82	+ 82	+ 74

1.	6 × 3	3 × 3	11 × 3	4 × 3	0 × 3	10 × 3	9 × 3
2.	0 × 3	4 × 3	11 × 3	3 × 3	6 × 3	9 × 3	10 × 3
3.	7 × 3	9 × 3	2 × 3	8 × 3	1 × 3	12 × 3	5 × 3
4.	9 × 3	7 × 3	5 × 3	12 × 3	1 × 3	8 × 3	2 × 3

5.	227 + 248	144 + 595	423 + 486	547 + 229	448 + 249
6.	659 + 227	671 + 247	529 + 359	263 + 655	227 + 659
7.	229 + 468	528 + 248	142 + 767	484 + 255	146 + 329

"The fishes of the sea shall declare unto thee . . ." Job 12:8

8. 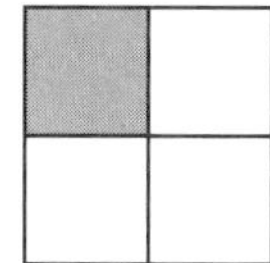  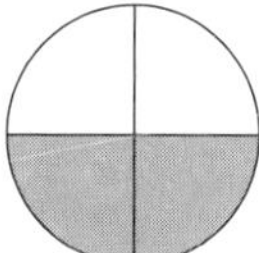 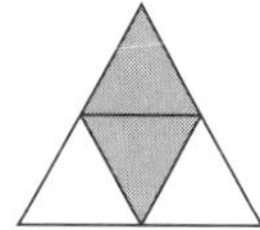

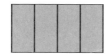

9. 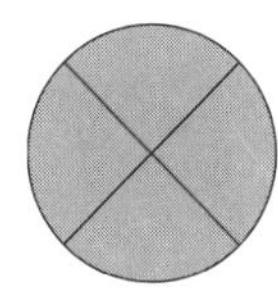 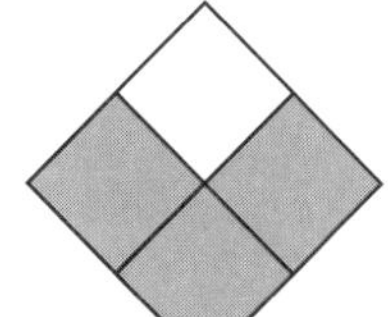 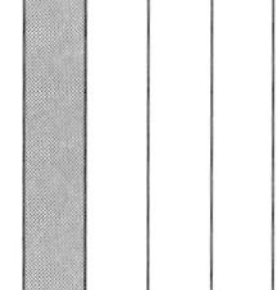 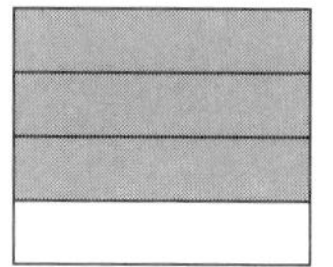

10. Every chapter in the Bible is from God. 50 chapters are in the first book of the Bible. 22 chapters are in the last book. How many more chapters are 50 than 22?

11. Ann has 23 uncles, and Fay has 19. How many more uncles has Ann than Fay?

12. Mighty waves swept up 97 crab shells and 53 snail shells. What was the difference in the number of shells?

13. Lester and Dean helped a widow to rake leaves. Lester raked 24 baskets, and Dean raked 18 baskets. How many more baskets did Lester rake than Dean?

1. 9×3 6×3 3×3 10×3 7×3 12×3 4×3

2. 6×3 9×3 10×3 3×3 12×3 7×3 4×3

3. 8×3 2×3 9×3 1×3 11×3 5×3 0×3

4. 2×3 8×3 1×3 9×3 5×3 11×3 0×3

5. $675 + 254$ $245 + 594$ $528 + 267$ $462 + 495$ $729 + 248$

6. $455 + 274$ $142 + 486$ $572 + 376$ $286 + 342$ $247 + 382$

7. $564 + 275$ $264 + 665$ $261 + 696$ $247 + 548$ $448 + 529$

"The fishes of the sea shall declare unto thee . . ." Job 12:8

8.  

9.   

10.	17 - 9 + 7 =	15 - 8 + 6 =
11.	7 + 9 - 8 =	6 + 7 - 5 =
12.	12 - 8 + 9 =	17 - 8 + 6 =
13.	16 - 7 + 5 =	5 + 7 - 3 =
14.	6 + 9 - 7 =	5 + 8 - 5 =
15.	7 + 7 - 5 =	12 - 4 + 6 =

16. 55 cows are brown and 27 are black. How many more cows are brown than black?

1. 8×3 3×3 6×1 7×3 0×3 12×3 6×3

2. 10×3 9×3 8×1 4×3 11×3 9×1 5×3

3. 5×3 3×3 11×3 12×1 8×1 9×3 10×3

4. 6×3 12×3 0×1 7×3 2×3 9×1 8×3

5. $687 + 292$ $475 + 108$ $175 + 793$ $258 + 234$ $375 + 482$

6. $373 + 274$ $626 + 364$ $294 + 392$ $463 + 527$ $262 + 385$

7. $337 + 246$ $496 + 483$ $143 + 349$ $393 + 575$ $584 + 273$

"The fishes of the sea shall declare unto thee . . ." Job 12:8

8. $8 + 6 - 5 =$ $8 + 4 - 6 =$

9. $15 - 8 + 6 =$ $17 - 9 + 7 =$

10. $16 - 9 + 8 =$ $14 - 8 + 5 =$

11. $5 + 8 - 7 =$ $3 + 8 - 2 =$

12. Beth sang to her baby sister for 35 minutes. She dusted for 27 minutes. How many more minutes did she sing than dust?

13. God made many kinds of fish. 36 kinds swam in a river. 19 kinds swam in a lake. What was the difference in the number of kinds?

14. 25 archer-fish shot water at beetles. 37 archer-fish shot water at spiders. What was the sum of fish that shot water?

1.	9 × 3	2 × 3	9 × 2	8 × 3	5 × 2	10 × 3	0 × 3
2.	6 × 1	9 × 3	0 × 2	10 × 3	10 × 1	8 × 3	9 × 2
3.	7 × 3	6 × 2	11 × 3	8 × 2	4 × 3	3 × 3	8 × 3
4.	12 × 1	7 × 3	8 × 3	9 × 1	4 × 3	8 × 2	11 × 3
5.	7 × 2	6 × 3	10 × 2	11 × 2	12 × 3	5 × 3	1 × 3
6.	6 × 3	7 × 2	1 × 3	5 × 3	12 × 3	11 × 2	10 × 2
7.	4 × 2	8 × 3	7 × 3	12 × 2	7 × 3	8 × 3	4 × 2

"The hand of the LORD hath wrought this." Job 12:9

51

1.
$$\begin{array}{r} 9 \\ \times\,3 \end{array} \quad \begin{array}{r} 2 \\ \times\,3 \end{array} \quad \begin{array}{r} 9 \\ \times\,2 \end{array} \quad \begin{array}{r} 8 \\ \times\,3 \end{array} \quad \begin{array}{r} 5 \\ \times\,2 \end{array} \quad \begin{array}{r} 10 \\ \times\,3 \end{array} \quad \begin{array}{r} 0 \\ \times\,3 \end{array}$$

2.
$$\begin{array}{r} 6 \\ \times\,1 \end{array} \quad \begin{array}{r} 9 \\ \times\,3 \end{array} \quad \begin{array}{r} 0 \\ \times\,2 \end{array} \quad \begin{array}{r} 10 \\ \times\,3 \end{array} \quad \begin{array}{r} 10 \\ \times\,1 \end{array} \quad \begin{array}{r} 8 \\ \times\,3 \end{array} \quad \begin{array}{r} 9 \\ \times\,2 \end{array}$$

3.
$$\begin{array}{r} 7 \\ \times\,3 \end{array} \quad \begin{array}{r} 6 \\ \times\,2 \end{array} \quad \begin{array}{r} 11 \\ \times\,3 \end{array} \quad \begin{array}{r} 8 \\ \times\,2 \end{array} \quad \begin{array}{r} 4 \\ \times\,3 \end{array} \quad \begin{array}{r} 3 \\ \times\,3 \end{array} \quad \begin{array}{r} 8 \\ \times\,3 \end{array}$$

4.
$$\begin{array}{r} 12 \\ \times\,1 \end{array} \quad \begin{array}{r} 7 \\ \times\,3 \end{array} \quad \begin{array}{r} 8 \\ \times\,3 \end{array} \quad \begin{array}{r} 9 \\ \times\,1 \end{array} \quad \begin{array}{r} 4 \\ \times\,3 \end{array} \quad \begin{array}{r} 8 \\ \times\,2 \end{array} \quad \begin{array}{r} 11 \\ \times\,3 \end{array}$$

5.
$$\begin{array}{r} 7 \\ \times\,2 \end{array} \quad \begin{array}{r} 6 \\ \times\,3 \end{array} \quad \begin{array}{r} 10 \\ \times\,2 \end{array} \quad \begin{array}{r} 11 \\ \times\,2 \end{array} \quad \begin{array}{r} 12 \\ \times\,3 \end{array} \quad \begin{array}{r} 5 \\ \times\,3 \end{array} \quad \begin{array}{r} 1 \\ \times\,3 \end{array}$$

6.
$$\begin{array}{r} 6 \\ \times\,3 \end{array} \quad \begin{array}{r} 7 \\ \times\,2 \end{array} \quad \begin{array}{r} 1 \\ \times\,3 \end{array} \quad \begin{array}{r} 5 \\ \times\,3 \end{array} \quad \begin{array}{r} 12 \\ \times\,3 \end{array} \quad \begin{array}{r} 11 \\ \times\,2 \end{array} \quad \begin{array}{r} 10 \\ \times\,2 \end{array}$$

7.
$$\begin{array}{r} 4 \\ \times\,2 \end{array} \quad \begin{array}{r} 8 \\ \times\,3 \end{array} \quad \begin{array}{r} 7 \\ \times\,3 \end{array} \quad \begin{array}{r} 12 \\ \times\,2 \end{array} \quad \begin{array}{r} 7 \\ \times\,3 \end{array} \quad \begin{array}{r} 8 \\ \times\,3 \end{array} \quad \begin{array}{r} 4 \\ \times\,2 \end{array}$$

"The hand of the LORD hath wrought this."   Job 12:9

8. 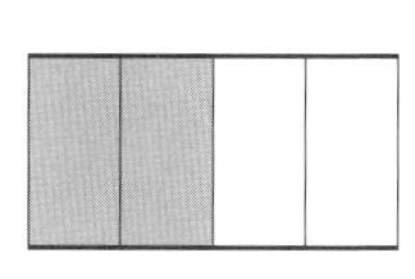 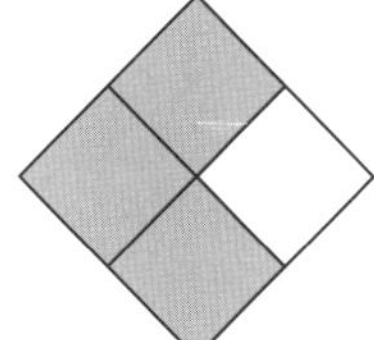 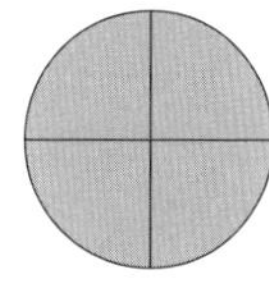 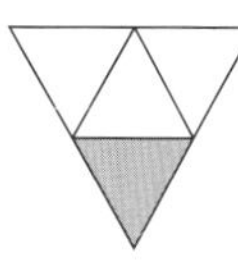

9. 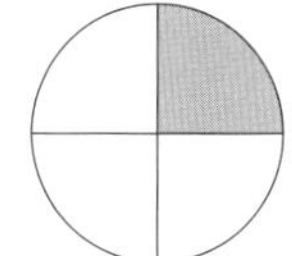 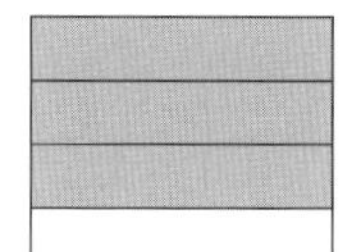 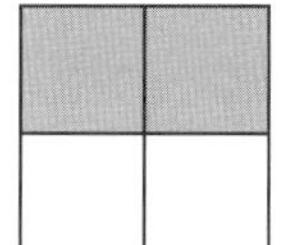 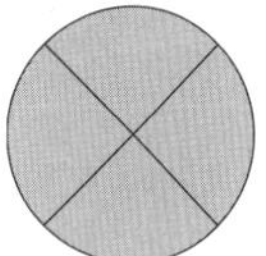

10.

708	906	605	807	409
- 395	- 662	- 174	- 584	- 253

11.

304	708	908	805	908
- 142	- 334	- 138	- 431	- 746

12.

708	909	707	609	808
- 485	- 478	- 463	- 296	- 652

13.

705	809	909	707	806
- 323	- 565	- 142	- 462	- 423

14. God gives us 24 hours at a time to work and play and sleep. How many days is that? *Write the rule.*

1.	8 × 3	3 × 3	3 × 2	10 × 3	2 × 3	3 × 3	12 × 2
2.	9 × 3	2 × 2	0 × 1	3 × 2	9 × 3	8 × 1	7 × 3
3.	7 × 3	4 × 2	9 × 3	2 × 3	0 × 3	4 × 1	9 × 3
4.	6 × 3	5 × 2	8 × 3	12 × 3	8 × 3	10 × 1	9 × 2
5.	5 × 3	1 × 3	0 × 2	4 × 3	11 × 2	7 × 3	7 × 2
6.	7 × 2	7 × 3	11 × 2	12 × 1	0 × 3	3 × 1	5 × 3
7.	4 × 3	8 × 2	5 × 3	11 × 3	5 × 3	8 × 2	6 × 2

"The hand of the LORD hath wrought this." Job 12:9

8. $2 \times 4 + 1 =$ $3 \times 7 + 1 =$

9. $2 \times 0 + 1 =$ $3 \times 8 + 1 =$

10. $2 \times 7 + 1 =$ $3 \times 9 + 1 =$

11. $3 \times 5 + 1 =$ $2 \times 9 + 1 =$

12. $2 \times 8 + 1 =$ $3 \times 6 + 1 =$

13.   

14.   

15. God made thousands of kinds of birds and fish in 1 day. How many hours were in that day? *Write the rule.*

1.	7×3	9×2	5×3	1×3	8×2	9×3	9×1
2.	0×3	9×3	7×2	5×2	8×3	2×3	4×3
3.	9×3	0×2	5×2	7×2	3×2	12×2	6×2
4.	3×3	9×3	8×2	3×1	5×3	6×3	7×3
5.	34×2	33×3	63×2	31×3	90×2	84×1	
6.	90×2	71×2	82×2	92×3	74×2	60×3	
7.	42×2	60×3	93×1	42×3	99×1	68×1	

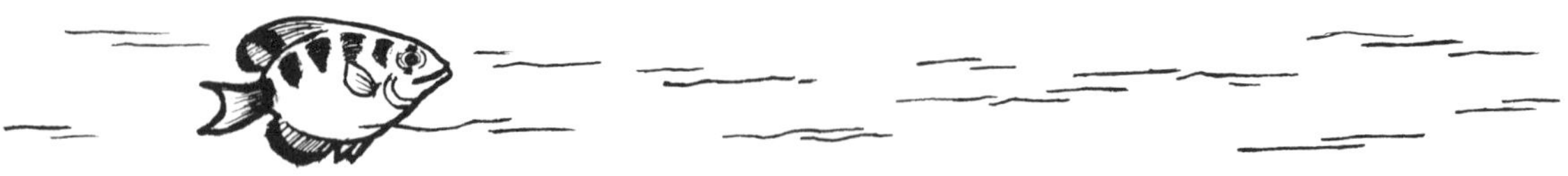

"The hand of the LORD hath wrought this." Job 12:9

8. $2 \times 3 + 1 =$ $3 \times 4 + 1 =$

9. $3 \times 3 + 1 =$ $2 \times 5 + 1 =$

10. $3 \times 0 + 1 =$ $3 \times 1 + 1 =$

11. $2 \times 2 + 1 =$ $2 \times 9 + 1 =$

12. two thousand, sixty-eight

13. two thousand, forty-three

14. one thousand, twenty-five

15. one thousand, fifty-two

16. two thousand, thirty-four

17. two thousand, eighty-six

18.

803	809	906	508	809
- 772	- 355	- 246	- 463	- 496

1. 4×3 9×3 8×2 7×3 2×3 12×3 6×3

2. 9×3 6×2 9×2 12×3 3×2 7×3 8×2

3. 5×3 9×3 12×2 9×1 11×3 7×2 5×2

4. 11×3 3×3 8×3 9×3 5×3 10×1 7×2

5. 92×3 94×2 53×3 83×2 71×3 80×1

6. 70×3 43×3 62×2 81×3 93×3 74×2

7. 93×3 59×1 60×3 54×2 61×3 82×3

"The hand of the LORD hath wrought this." Job 12:9

8. God lit the night sky. Ray looked up. He counted seven stars in the Big Dipper and six stars in the Little Dipper. How many more stars are seven than six?

9. Keith gave 23 mints to his sister Lois, and he kept 17. Lois has how many more mints than Keith?

10. Archer-fish ate 33 green bugs, 42 black bugs, and 54 red bugs. What sum of bugs did the fish eat?

11. The wind hummed through 56 pine trees and 38 fir trees. What was the difference in the number of trees?

12. Wilmer sang 3 songs as he swept the barn, 5 songs as he fed the hogs, and 7 songs as he rode his bike. What sum of songs did he sing?

55

1. 0×4 $\quad 1 \times 4$ $\quad 2 \times 4$ $\quad 3 \times 4$ $\quad 4 \times 4$ $\quad 5 \times 4$ $\quad 6 \times 4$

2. 7×4 $\quad 8 \times 4$ $\quad 9 \times 4$ $\quad 10 \times 4$ $\quad 11 \times 4$ $\quad 12 \times 4$

3. 5×4 $\quad 2 \times 4$ $\quad 6 \times 4$ $\quad 8 \times 4$ $\quad 10 \times 4$ $\quad 3 \times 4$ $\quad 1 \times 4$

4. 2×4 $\quad 5 \times 4$ $\quad 4 \times 4$ $\quad 7 \times 4$ $\quad 9 \times 4$ $\quad 11 \times 4$ $\quad 8 \times 4$

5. 12×4 $\quad 9 \times 4$ $\quad 6 \times 4$ $\quad 0 \times 4$ $\quad 6 \times 4$ $\quad 9 \times 4$ $\quad 12 \times 4$

6. 7×4 $\quad 4 \times 4$ $\quad 8 \times 4$ $\quad 11 \times 4$ $\quad 9 \times 4$ $\quad 7 \times 4$ $\quad 4 \times 4$

7. 4×4 $\quad 7 \times 4$ $\quad 1 \times 4$ $\quad 3 \times 4$ $\quad 10 \times 4$ $\quad 8 \times 4$ $\quad 6 \times 4$

"Power belongeth unto God." Psalm 62:11

55

1.
$$\begin{array}{r}0\\\times 4\\\hline\end{array}\qquad\begin{array}{r}1\\\times 4\\\hline\end{array}\qquad\begin{array}{r}2\\\times 4\\\hline\end{array}\qquad\begin{array}{r}3\\\times 4\\\hline\end{array}\qquad\begin{array}{r}4\\\times 4\\\hline\end{array}\qquad\begin{array}{r}5\\\times 4\\\hline\end{array}\qquad\begin{array}{r}6\\\times 4\\\hline\end{array}$$

2.
$$\begin{array}{r}7\\\times 4\\\hline\end{array}\qquad\begin{array}{r}8\\\times 4\\\hline\end{array}\qquad\begin{array}{r}9\\\times 4\\\hline\end{array}\qquad\begin{array}{r}10\\\times 4\\\hline\end{array}\qquad\begin{array}{r}11\\\times 4\\\hline\end{array}\qquad\begin{array}{r}12\\\times 4\\\hline\end{array}$$

3.
$$\begin{array}{r}5\\\times 4\\\hline\end{array}\qquad\begin{array}{r}2\\\times 4\\\hline\end{array}\qquad\begin{array}{r}6\\\times 4\\\hline\end{array}\qquad\begin{array}{r}8\\\times 4\\\hline\end{array}\qquad\begin{array}{r}10\\\times 4\\\hline\end{array}\qquad\begin{array}{r}3\\\times 4\\\hline\end{array}\qquad\begin{array}{r}1\\\times 4\\\hline\end{array}$$

4.
$$\begin{array}{r}2\\\times 4\\\hline\end{array}\qquad\begin{array}{r}5\\\times 4\\\hline\end{array}\qquad\begin{array}{r}4\\\times 4\\\hline\end{array}\qquad\begin{array}{r}7\\\times 4\\\hline\end{array}\qquad\begin{array}{r}9\\\times 4\\\hline\end{array}\qquad\begin{array}{r}11\\\times 4\\\hline\end{array}\qquad\begin{array}{r}8\\\times 4\\\hline\end{array}$$

5.
$$\begin{array}{r}12\\\times 4\\\hline\end{array}\qquad\begin{array}{r}9\\\times 4\\\hline\end{array}\qquad\begin{array}{r}6\\\times 4\\\hline\end{array}\qquad\begin{array}{r}0\\\times 4\\\hline\end{array}\qquad\begin{array}{r}6\\\times 4\\\hline\end{array}\qquad\begin{array}{r}9\\\times 4\\\hline\end{array}\qquad\begin{array}{r}12\\\times 4\\\hline\end{array}$$

6.
$$\begin{array}{r}7\\\times 4\\\hline\end{array}\qquad\begin{array}{r}4\\\times 4\\\hline\end{array}\qquad\begin{array}{r}8\\\times 4\\\hline\end{array}\qquad\begin{array}{r}11\\\times 4\\\hline\end{array}\qquad\begin{array}{r}9\\\times 4\\\hline\end{array}\qquad\begin{array}{r}7\\\times 4\\\hline\end{array}\qquad\begin{array}{r}4\\\times 4\\\hline\end{array}$$

7.
$$\begin{array}{r}4\\\times 4\\\hline\end{array}\qquad\begin{array}{r}7\\\times 4\\\hline\end{array}\qquad\begin{array}{r}1\\\times 4\\\hline\end{array}\qquad\begin{array}{r}3\\\times 4\\\hline\end{array}\qquad\begin{array}{r}10\\\times 4\\\hline\end{array}\qquad\begin{array}{r}8\\\times 4\\\hline\end{array}\qquad\begin{array}{r}6\\\times 4\\\hline\end{array}$$

"Power belongeth unto God."   Psalm 62:11

8. 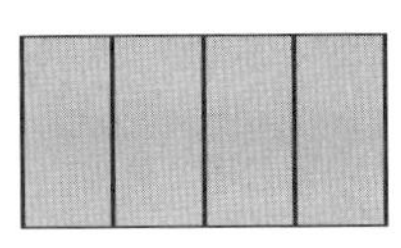 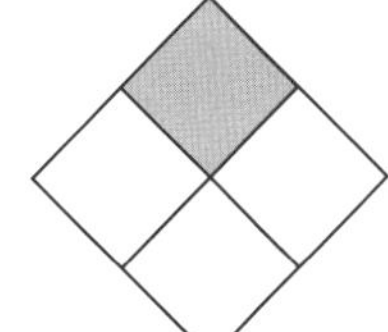 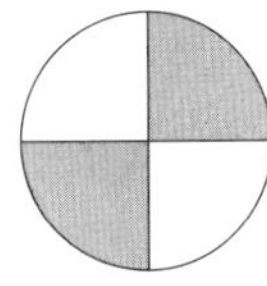 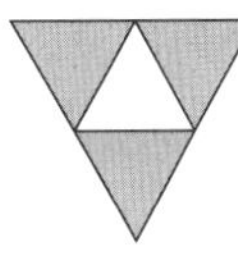

9. 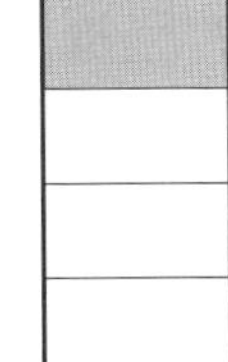 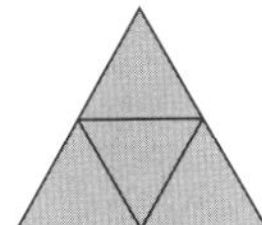 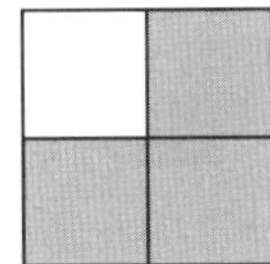 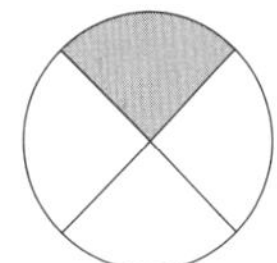

10. The Bible says that God made the sun stand still for about 1 day. About how many hours was that? *Write the rule.*

11. Beth mailed a letter to Grandmother. It took 24 hours for Grandmother to get the letter. How many days was that? *Write the rule.*

12.

23	32	62	32	35	53
65	34	23	63	44	26
+ 69	+ 78	+ 24	+ 43	+ 66	+ 79

13.

41	14	55	23	14	31
35	73	21	24	51	42
+ 94	+ 75	+ 63	+ 33	+ 98	+ 98

1.

2	4	8	12	1	3	6
× 4	× 4	× 4	× 4	× 4	× 4	× 4

2.

0	9	11	7	5	6	3
× 4	× 4	× 4	× 4	× 4	× 4	× 4

3.

5	7	11	9	0	9	10
× 4	× 4	× 4	× 4	× 4	× 4	× 4

4.

1	12	8	4	2	10	9
× 4	× 4	× 4	× 4	× 4	× 4	× 4

5.

68	84	92	37	86	93
+ 39	− 27	− 78	+ 68	− 58	− 46

6.

37	26	80	72	35	29
+ 59	+ 58	− 44	− 35	+ 49	+ 67

7.

93	29	84	97	56	83
− 36	+ 78	− 37	− 69	+ 49	− 69

"Power belongeth unto God." Psalm 62:11

8.   

9.   

10. God is always the same. But people grow old. Grandfather is 90 years old. Father is 53 years old. How many years older is Grandfather than Father?

11. 33 baby croc-o-diles hatched in a nest. The mother took 15 babies to the river in her mouth. How many babies were still in the nest?

12. A croc-o-dile bird flew for 28 minutes. It pecked bugs for 13 minutes. What was the difference in the number of minutes?

1.	6	9	4	8	2	10	5
	× 4	× 4	× 4	× 4	× 4	× 4	× 4
2.	9	6	8	4	10	2	5
	× 4	× 4	× 4	× 4	× 4	× 4	× 4
3.	0	7	11	9	1	12	3
	× 4	× 4	× 4	× 4	× 4	× 4	× 4
4.	7	0	9	11	12	1	3
	× 4	× 4	× 4	× 4	× 4	× 4	× 4

5.	75	23	79	99	37	80
	− 28	+ 86	+ 25	− 43	+ 45	− 44
6.	52	85	28	39	60	84
	+ 94	− 58	+ 69	+ 59	− 32	+ 63
7.	75	86	78	57	94	53
	+ 34	− 39	− 22	+ 47	− 58	+ 29

"Power belongeth unto God." Psalm 62:11

8. 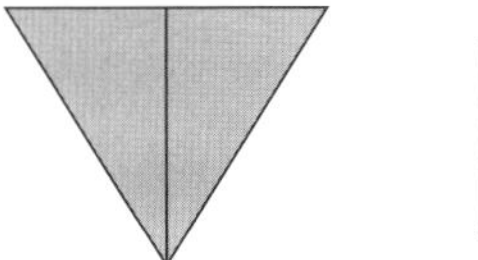 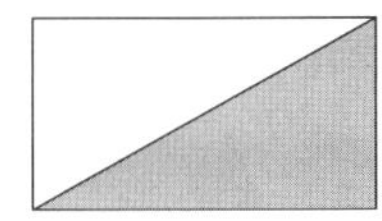  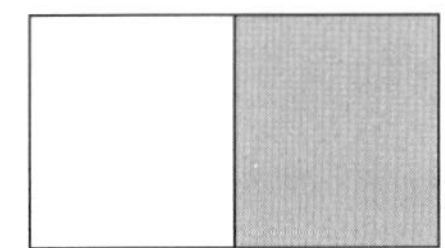

9. 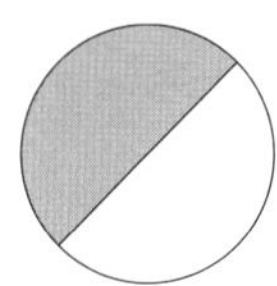 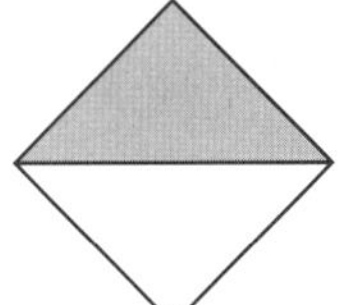 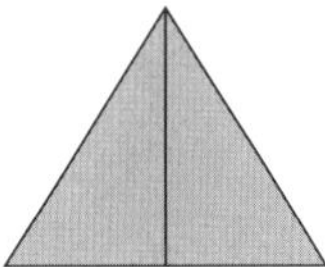 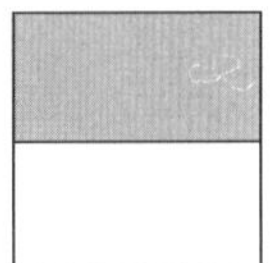

10. two thousand, five hundred four

11. one thousand, seven hundred seven

12. two thousand, three hundred two

13. one thousand, nine hundred eight

14. $4 \times 5 + 1 =$ $4 \times 4 + 1 =$

15. $4 \times 9 + 1 =$ $4 \times 10 + 1 =$

16. $4 \times 6 + 1 =$ $4 \times 7 + 1 =$

17. $4 \times 12 + 1 =$ $4 \times 11 + 1 =$

18. $4 \times 3 + 1 =$ $4 \times 8 + 1 =$

1.

6	9	0	12	8	10	7
× 4	× 4	× 1	× 4	× 4	× 4	× 4

2.

3	10	2	8	1	11	8
× 4	× 2	× 4	× 4	× 4	× 4	× 2

3.

7	10	8	12	0	9	12
× 4	× 4	× 4	× 4	× 4	× 4	× 2

4.

4	11	2	8	4	5	6
× 4	× 4	× 2	× 4	× 2	× 4	× 2

5.

58	34	99	66	36	75
+ 28	+ 26	− 62	− 47	+ 67	− 38

6.

23	89	67	32	91	19
+ 65	− 55	+ 39	+ 73	− 58	+ 68

7.

86	65	87	67	33	39
− 49	+ 38	− 68	− 30	+ 27	+ 47

"Power belongeth unto God." Psalm 62:11

8. 1 quarter + 13 nickels   2 quarters + 9 nickels

9. 6 dimes + 5 nickels   3 quarters + 2 dimes

10. 2 quarters + 6 nickels   11 nickels + 39 pennies

11. 7 nickels + 27 pennies   3 quarters + 18 pennies

12.

13.

14. It took 1 day for paint to dry on the church steps. How many hours was that? *Write the rule.*

59

1.	9 × 4	8 × 3	10 × 2	10 × 4	5 × 4	6 × 4	12 × 3
2.	8 × 4	11 × 4	4 × 3	12 × 1	1 × 4	0 × 3	2 × 4
3.	7 × 4	12 × 4	3 × 3	9 × 2	9 × 3	12 × 3	5 × 3
4.	12 × 2	4 × 4	7 × 3	5 × 2	11 × 2	9 × 4	6 × 1
5.	2 × 3	9 × 4	11 × 2	10 × 1	7 × 3	8 × 2	6 × 4
6.	5 × 3	12 × 3	9 × 3	6 × 3	9 × 1	12 × 4	7 × 4
7.	4 × 2	0 × 4	2 × 2	6 × 2	3 × 4	11 × 4	8 × 4

"Power belongeth unto God." Psalm 62:11

8. 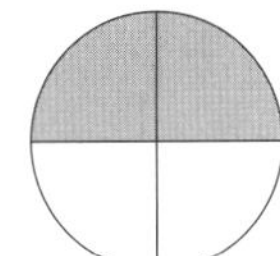 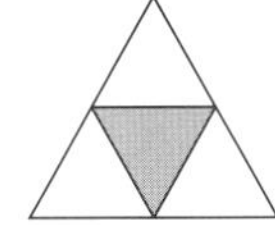 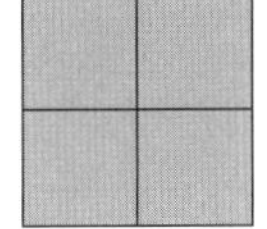 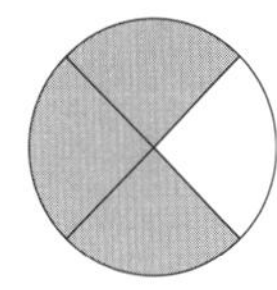

9.

808	903	709	605	906
- 475	- 338	- 457	- 139	- 219

10.

809	602	909	802	807
- 243	- 268	- 442	- 549	- 119

11. It takes Fay 28 minutes to get to school and 13 minutes to get to church. How many more minutes is 28 than 13?

12. A minister preached about God's might. He read 25 verses from Psalms and 19 verses from Isaiah. What was the sum of verses that he read?

1. 8 12 7 4 8 7 0
× 4 × 3 × 3 × 3 × 2 × 4 × 1

2. 9 6 5 3 10 8 9
× 3 × 4 × 4 × 3 × 2 × 3 × 3

3. 7 4 3 7 9 8 0
× 4 × 4 × 4 × 3 × 4 × 4 × 4

4. 8 7 6 7 5 6 9
× 4 × 4 × 4 × 3 × 4 × 3 × 3

5. 9 12 4 5 3 3 2
× 4 × 4 × 4 × 3 × 4 × 3 × 4

6. 9 9 10 7 8 7 8
× 3 × 2 × 2 × 3 × 3 × 4 × 4

7. 4 3 4 5 8 12 12
× 2 × 3 × 3 × 3 × 2 × 4 × 3

"Power belongeth unto God." Psalm 62:11

8. 

9.  

10. 18 − 9 + 8 = 6 + 9 − 7 =

11. 7 + 8 − 9 = 12 − 8 + 9 =

12. 14 − 6 + 5 = 5 + 8 − 7 =

13. 9 + 7 − 8 = 16 − 7 + 8 =

14. 15 children stand up straight in a line. In another line 17 children stand up straight. How many children is that altogether?

15. Twenty croc-o-diles rest in a nook. A mighty wave sweeps nine of them to other homes. How many croc-o-diles are still in the nook?

61

1.

8 × 3	5 × 4	6 × 3	3 × 4	4 × 4	7 × 3	12 × 2

2.

3 × 3	2 × 4	12 × 4	10 × 4	12 × 4	4 × 2	3 × 3

3.

6 × 4	7 × 3	8 × 2	4 × 3	9 × 2	10 × 2	6 × 4

4.

93 × 3	92 × 2	81 × 3	52 × 3	74 × 2	40 × 3

5.

62 × 3	51 × 2	73 × 3	84 × 2	92 × 3	83 × 3

6.

92 × 2	93 × 3	60 × 2	74 × 2	52 × 3	81 × 3

7.

51 × 2	93 × 2	83 × 3	92 × 3	84 × 2	73 × 3

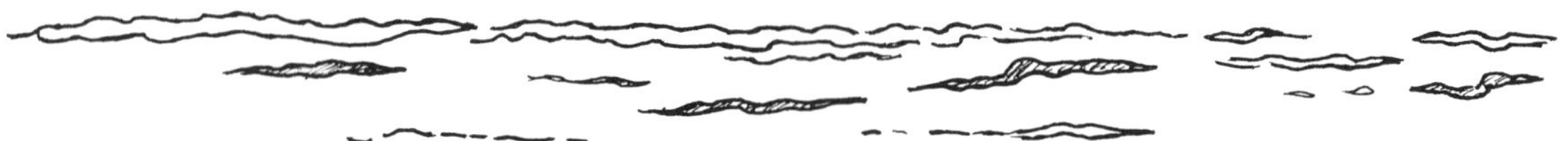

8. 

9.  

10. $2 \times 10 + 1 =$ $\quad$ $3 \times 10 + 1 =$

11. $2 \times 11 + 1 =$ $\quad$ $3 \times 11 + 1 =$

12. $3 \times 9 + 1 =$ $\quad$ $3 \times 12 + 1 =$

13. $2 \times 8 + 1 =$ $\quad$ $2 \times 9 + 1 =$

14. $3 \times 8 + 1 =$

"The LORD on high is mightier than . . .
the mighty waves of the sea."
Psalm 93:4

62

1. 12×4 6×4 10×2 11×4 8×4 12×3 7×4

2. 6×3 4×4 12×1 4×3 8×2 9×2 0×1

3. 5×4 8×3 12×4 9×4 8×4 11×4 7×4

4. 82×4 62×3 91×4 84×2 42×3 60×4

5. 70×4 93×3 71×3 32×4 90×3 51×4

6. 91×4 93×2 82×4 80×3 63×2 42×4

7. 71×3 93×3 70×4 51×4 90×3 32×4

"Power belongeth unto God." Psalm 62:11

1.
$$\begin{array}{r}12\\ \times\ 4\\ \hline\end{array}\qquad\begin{array}{r}6\\ \times\ 4\\ \hline\end{array}\qquad\begin{array}{r}10\\ \times\ 2\\ \hline\end{array}\qquad\begin{array}{r}11\\ \times\ 4\\ \hline\end{array}\qquad\begin{array}{r}8\\ \times\ 4\\ \hline\end{array}\qquad\begin{array}{r}12\\ \times\ 3\\ \hline\end{array}\qquad\begin{array}{r}7\\ \times\ 4\\ \hline\end{array}$$

2.
$$\begin{array}{r}6\\ \times\ 3\\ \hline\end{array}\qquad\begin{array}{r}4\\ \times\ 4\\ \hline\end{array}\qquad\begin{array}{r}12\\ \times\ 1\\ \hline\end{array}\qquad\begin{array}{r}4\\ \times\ 3\\ \hline\end{array}\qquad\begin{array}{r}8\\ \times\ 2\\ \hline\end{array}\qquad\begin{array}{r}9\\ \times\ 2\\ \hline\end{array}\qquad\begin{array}{r}0\\ \times\ 1\\ \hline\end{array}$$

3.
$$\begin{array}{r}5\\ \times\ 4\\ \hline\end{array}\qquad\begin{array}{r}8\\ \times\ 3\\ \hline\end{array}\qquad\begin{array}{r}12\\ \times\ 4\\ \hline\end{array}\qquad\begin{array}{r}9\\ \times\ 4\\ \hline\end{array}\qquad\begin{array}{r}8\\ \times\ 4\\ \hline\end{array}\qquad\begin{array}{r}11\\ \times\ 4\\ \hline\end{array}\qquad\begin{array}{r}7\\ \times\ 4\\ \hline\end{array}$$

4.
$$\begin{array}{r}82\\ \times\ 4\\ \hline\end{array}\qquad\begin{array}{r}62\\ \times\ 3\\ \hline\end{array}\qquad\begin{array}{r}91\\ \times\ 4\\ \hline\end{array}\qquad\begin{array}{r}84\\ \times\ 2\\ \hline\end{array}\qquad\begin{array}{r}42\\ \times\ 3\\ \hline\end{array}\qquad\begin{array}{r}60\\ \times\ 4\\ \hline\end{array}$$

5.
$$\begin{array}{r}70\\ \times\ 4\\ \hline\end{array}\qquad\begin{array}{r}93\\ \times\ 3\\ \hline\end{array}\qquad\begin{array}{r}71\\ \times\ 3\\ \hline\end{array}\qquad\begin{array}{r}32\\ \times\ 4\\ \hline\end{array}\qquad\begin{array}{r}90\\ \times\ 3\\ \hline\end{array}\qquad\begin{array}{r}51\\ \times\ 4\\ \hline\end{array}$$

6.
$$\begin{array}{r}91\\ \times\ 4\\ \hline\end{array}\qquad\begin{array}{r}93\\ \times\ 2\\ \hline\end{array}\qquad\begin{array}{r}82\\ \times\ 4\\ \hline\end{array}\qquad\begin{array}{r}80\\ \times\ 3\\ \hline\end{array}\qquad\begin{array}{r}63\\ \times\ 2\\ \hline\end{array}\qquad\begin{array}{r}42\\ \times\ 4\\ \hline\end{array}$$

7.
$$\begin{array}{r}71\\ \times\ 3\\ \hline\end{array}\qquad\begin{array}{r}93\\ \times\ 3\\ \hline\end{array}\qquad\begin{array}{r}70\\ \times\ 4\\ \hline\end{array}\qquad\begin{array}{r}51\\ \times\ 4\\ \hline\end{array}\qquad\begin{array}{r}90\\ \times\ 3\\ \hline\end{array}\qquad\begin{array}{r}32\\ \times\ 4\\ \hline\end{array}$$

"Power belongeth unto God." Psalm 62:11

8.  

9.   

10. one thousand, nineteen

11. two thousand, eighty-seven

12. two thousand, sixty-six

13. two thousand, forty-five

14. one thousand, twenty-three

---

15. A baby croc-o-dile can grow 12 inches in a year. How many feet is that? *Write the rule.*

16. A family Bible can be 1 foot long. How many inches is that? *Write the rule.*

63

1. $1\overline{)0}$ $1\overline{)1}$ $1\overline{)2}$ $1\overline{)3}$ $1\overline{)4}$

2. $1\overline{)5}$ $1\overline{)6}$ $1\overline{)7}$ $1\overline{)8}$ $1\overline{)9}$

3. $1\overline{)10}$ $1\overline{)11}$ $1\overline{)12}$

4. $1\overline{)2}$ $1\overline{)5}$ $1\overline{)9}$ $1\overline{)12}$ $1\overline{)0}$

5. $1\overline{)0}$ $1\overline{)12}$ $1\overline{)9}$ $1\overline{)5}$ $1\overline{)2}$

6. $1\overline{)0}$ $1\overline{)6}$ $1\overline{)8}$ $1\overline{)10}$ $1\overline{)3}$

7. $1\overline{)3}$ $1\overline{)10}$ $1\overline{)8}$ $1\overline{)6}$ $1\overline{)0}$

8. $1\overline{)1}$ $1\overline{)4}$ $1\overline{)7}$ $1\overline{)11}$ $1\overline{)9}$

9. $1\overline{)9}$ $1\overline{)11}$ $1\overline{)7}$ $1\overline{)4}$ $1\overline{)1}$

"Let the sea roar." Psalm 98:7

10. 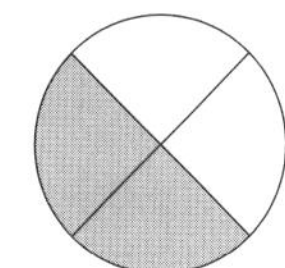 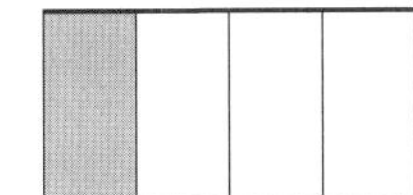 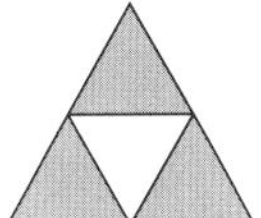 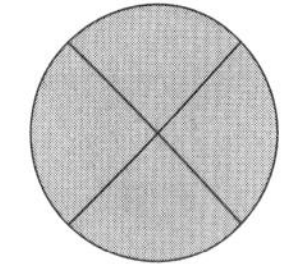

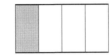

11. 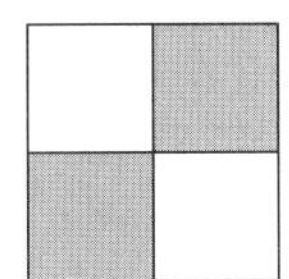 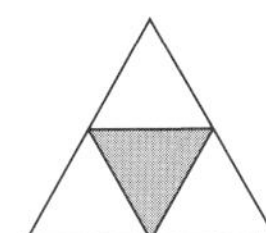 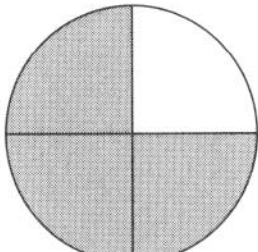 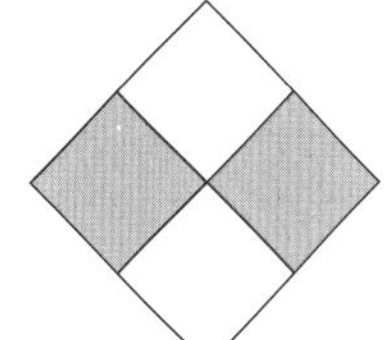

12.

35	33	43	34	25	14
12	25	24	35	12	62
+ 92	+ 36	+ 39	+ 49	+ 88	+ 73

13.

34	58	24	12	44	51
24	21	40	73	35	33
+ 89	+ 73	+ 63	+ 43	+ 74	+ 64

14.

63	12	21	22	23	33
24	37	75	20	13	52
+ 63	+ 77	+ 23	+ 65	+ 59	+ 55

15. Spring Hill Church made a scrapbook for their bishop's family. The scrapbook was 1 foot long. How many inches was that? *Write the rule.*

16. Father's shoe is 12 inches long. How many feet is that? *Write the rule.*

64

1. $2\overline{)0}$ $2\overline{)2}$ $2\overline{)4}$ $2\overline{)6}$ $2\overline{)8}$

2. $2\overline{)10}$ $2\overline{)12}$ $2\overline{)14}$ $2\overline{)16}$ $2\overline{)18}$

3. $2\overline{)20}$ $2\overline{)22}$ $2\overline{)24}$

4. $2\overline{)4}$ $2\overline{)10}$ $2\overline{)14}$ $2\overline{)22}$ $2\overline{)18}$

5. $2\overline{)18}$ $2\overline{)22}$ $2\overline{)14}$ $2\overline{)10}$ $2\overline{)4}$

6. $2\overline{)0}$ $2\overline{)6}$ $2\overline{)12}$ $2\overline{)16}$ $2\overline{)20}$

7. $2\overline{)20}$ $2\overline{)16}$ $2\overline{)12}$ $2\overline{)6}$ $2\overline{)0}$

8. $2\overline{)2}$ $2\overline{)8}$ $2\overline{)18}$ $2\overline{)24}$ $2\overline{)16}$

9. $2\overline{)16}$ $2\overline{)24}$ $2\overline{)18}$ $2\overline{)8}$ $2\overline{)2}$

"Let the sea roar." Psalm 98:7

10. 5 dimes + 7 nickels　　　2 quarters + 48 pennies

11. 13 nickels + 18 pennies　　　3 quarters + 4 nickels

12. 4 dimes + 8 nickels　　　2 dimes + 9 nickels

13. 2 quarters + 6 nickels　　　1 quarter + 5 nickels

14.   

15.  

16. Father planted a small tree that was 1 foot tall. How many inches tall was that? *Write the rule.*

1. 2)8 2)10 2)4 2)0 1)10
2. 2)10 1)4 1)0 1)2 2)16
3. 2)6 1)1 2)18 2)14 2)20
4. 2)2 1)3 1)7 1)9 1)8
5. 1)6 2)24 2)14 2)24 2)22
6. 2)24 2)12 2)24 2)14 2)0
7. 2)18 2)10 2)16 2)6 2)22
8. 2)10 2)18 1)3 2)16 1)0
9. 2)12 1)5 1)11 1)5 2)12

"Let the sea roar." Psalm 98:7

10. 

11. 

12.

908	705	606	708	707
- 432	- 469	- 279	- 245	- 459

13.

807	505	902	607	909
- 173	- 337	- 580	- 438	- 274

14.

806	606	505	404	809
- 558	- 143	- 178	- 168	- 333

15.

903	902	707	802	703
- 587	- 227	- 157	- 126	- 386

16. Chester worked on arithmetic for 30 minutes. He worked on spelling for 15 minutes. How many more minutes did he work on arithmetic than on spelling?

66

1.	$3\overline{)0}$	$3\overline{)3}$	$3\overline{)6}$	$3\overline{)9}$	$3\overline{)12}$
2.	$3\overline{)15}$	$3\overline{)18}$	$3\overline{)21}$	$3\overline{)24}$	$3\overline{)27}$
3.	$3\overline{)30}$	$3\overline{)33}$	$3\overline{)36}$		
4.	$3\overline{)6}$	$3\overline{)12}$	$3\overline{)15}$	$3\overline{)21}$	$3\overline{)27}$
5.	$3\overline{)3}$	$3\overline{)15}$	$3\overline{)18}$	$3\overline{)33}$	$3\overline{)24}$
6.	$3\overline{)0}$	$3\overline{)9}$	$3\overline{)24}$	$3\overline{)30}$	$3\overline{)36}$
7.	$3\overline{)36}$	$3\overline{)30}$	$3\overline{)24}$	$3\overline{)9}$	$3\overline{)0}$
8.	$3\overline{)24}$	$3\overline{)33}$	$3\overline{)18}$	$3\overline{)15}$	$3\overline{)3}$
9.	$3\overline{)27}$	$3\overline{)21}$	$3\overline{)15}$	$3\overline{)12}$	$3\overline{)6}$

"Let the sea roar." Psalm 98:7

10. 18 − 9 + 8 = 17 − 9 + 7 =

11. 7 + 8 − 6 = 15 − 8 + 7 =

12. 12 − 8 + 9 = 15 − 9 + 7 =

13. 13 − 5 + 6 = 8 + 8 − 9 =

14. 17 − 8 + 6 = 11 − 3 + 9 =

15. 6 + 9 − 7 = 4 + 8 − 7 =

16. 9 + 3 − 7 = 6 + 8 − 6 =

17. A minister flew by jet to visit churches in South America. It took 24 hours for him to get there. How many days was that? *Write the rule.*

18.

903	803	901	902	804
− 478	− 539	− 598	− 628	− 369

1.	$3\overline{)27}$	$3\overline{)18}$	$3\overline{)12}$	$3\overline{)30}$	$3\overline{)21}$
2.	$2\overline{)24}$	$3\overline{)9}$	$3\overline{)33}$	$3\overline{)3}$	$3\overline{)36}$
3.	$3\overline{)15}$	$3\overline{)6}$	$3\overline{)0}$	$3\overline{)6}$	$3\overline{)15}$
4.	$3\overline{)36}$	$3\overline{)3}$	$3\overline{)33}$	$3\overline{)9}$	$3\overline{)24}$
5.	$3\overline{)21}$	$3\overline{)30}$	$3\overline{)12}$	$3\overline{)18}$	$3\overline{)27}$
6.	$2\overline{)6}$	$1\overline{)9}$	$2\overline{)14}$	$2\overline{)10}$	$1\overline{)6}$
7.	$2\overline{)16}$	$2\overline{)0}$	$1\overline{)10}$	$2\overline{)24}$	$2\overline{)8}$
8.	$1\overline{)4}$	$1\overline{)12}$	$2\overline{)20}$	$1\overline{)0}$	$1\overline{)8}$
9.	$2\overline{)12}$	$1\overline{)5}$	$1\overline{)7}$	$2\overline{)18}$	$1\overline{)3}$

"Let the sea roar." Psalm 98:7

10. 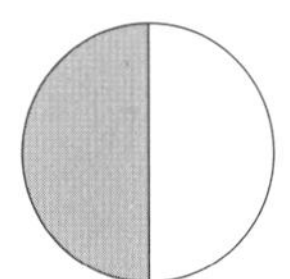 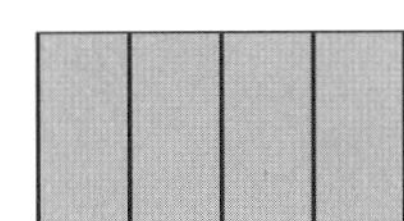 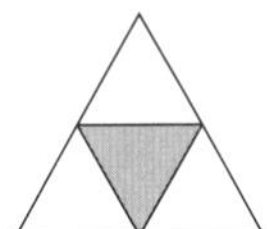 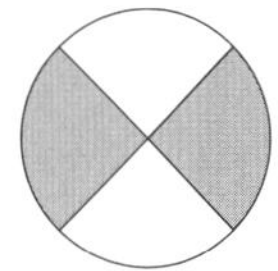

11. 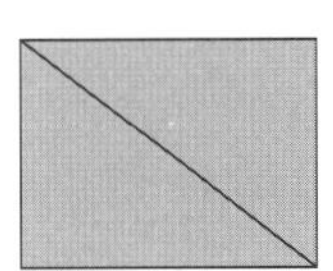 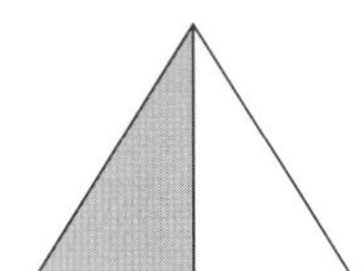 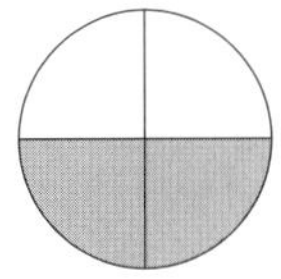 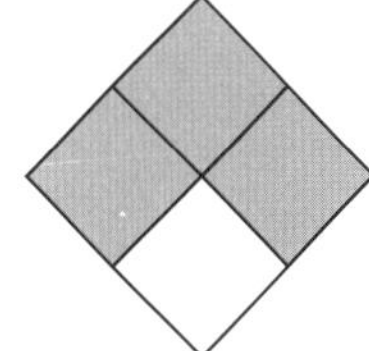

12.

806	770	707	508	990
- 438	- 235	- 449	- 229	- 577

13.

904	850	907	890	703
- 576	- 526	- 368	- 432	- 287

14.

780	704	707	802	890
- 522	- 169	- 339	- 389	- 611

15.

806	702	505	680	905
- 267	- 378	- 177	- 264	- 447

16. Jean is 17 years old. Her sister is 9 years old. How many years older is Jean than her sister?

17. Norman is 28 years old. Ray is 12 years old. How many years younger is Ray than Norman?

1.	$3\overline{)27}$	$2\overline{)14}$	$3\overline{)21}$	$2\overline{)22}$	$3\overline{)30}$
2.	$3\overline{)21}$	$2\overline{)18}$	$3\overline{)18}$	$3\overline{)36}$	$1\overline{)12}$
3.	$1\overline{)9}$	$3\overline{)24}$	$1\overline{)10}$	$3\overline{)33}$	$2\overline{)14}$
4.	$2\overline{)16}$	$3\overline{)27}$	$3\overline{)36}$	$2\overline{)24}$	$2\overline{)12}$
5.	$3\overline{)33}$	$3\overline{)9}$	$3\overline{)12}$	$1\overline{)5}$	$3\overline{)18}$
6.	$2\overline{)6}$	$1\overline{)11}$	$3\overline{)24}$	$3\overline{)36}$	$3\overline{)6}$
7.	$3\overline{)15}$	$2\overline{)20}$	$1\overline{)6}$	$3\overline{)15}$	$2\overline{)8}$
8.	$3\overline{)30}$	$2\overline{)10}$	$2\overline{)4}$	$3\overline{)36}$	$3\overline{)24}$
9.	$3\overline{)3}$	$3\overline{)21}$	$3\overline{)0}$	$1\overline{)7}$	$2\overline{)2}$

"Let the sea roar." Psalm 98:7

10. 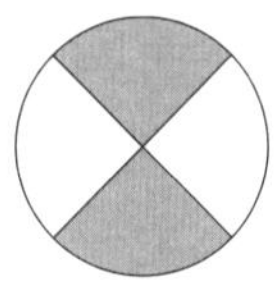 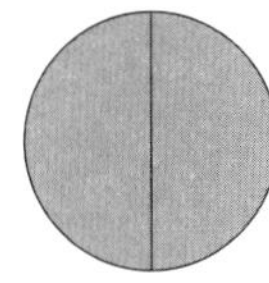 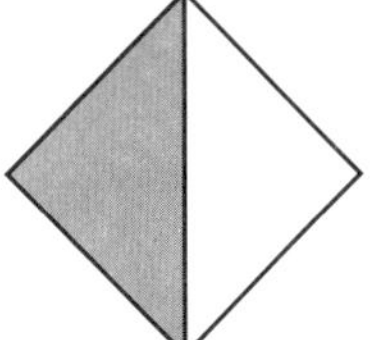 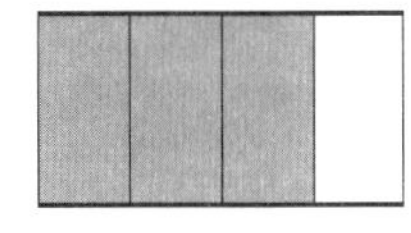

11. 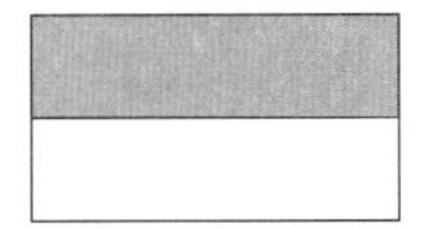 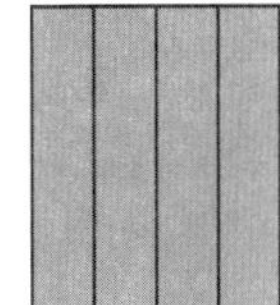 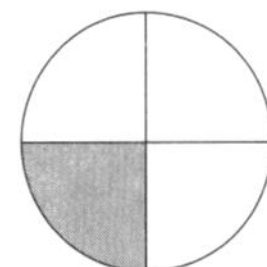 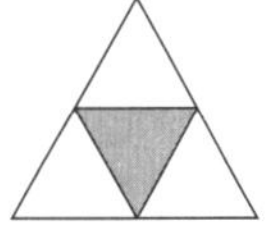

12. Father is 48 years old. Wilmer is 15 years old. How many years older is Father than Wilmer?

13. Grandmother is 65 years old. Lois is nine years old. How many years younger is Lois than Grandmother?

14.

$$\begin{array}{r} 708 \\ -\ 445 \\ \hline \end{array} \quad \begin{array}{r} 690 \\ -\ 243 \\ \hline \end{array} \quad \begin{array}{r} 770 \\ -\ 235 \\ \hline \end{array} \quad \begin{array}{r} 806 \\ -\ 438 \\ \hline \end{array} \quad \begin{array}{r} 602 \\ -\ 478 \\ \hline \end{array}$$

15.

$$\begin{array}{r} 909 \\ -\ 685 \\ \hline \end{array} \quad \begin{array}{r} 807 \\ -\ 339 \\ \hline \end{array} \quad \begin{array}{r} 909 \\ -\ 274 \\ \hline \end{array} \quad \begin{array}{r} 904 \\ -\ 357 \\ \hline \end{array} \quad \begin{array}{r} 990 \\ -\ 627 \\ \hline \end{array}$$

69

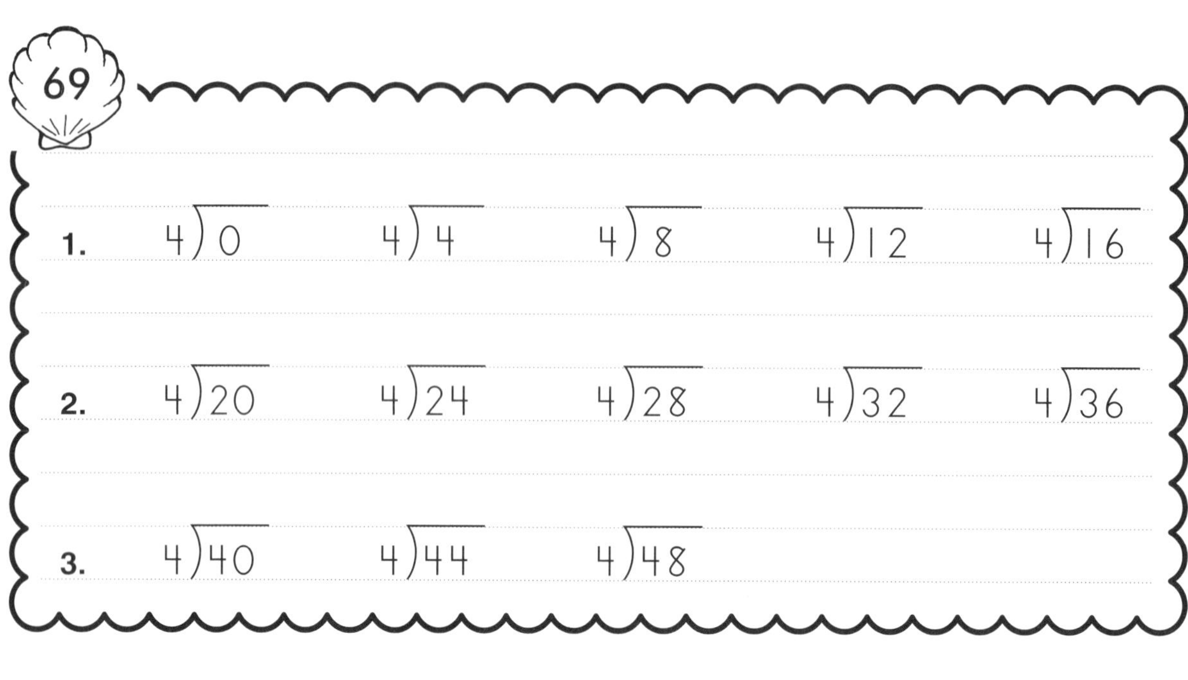

1. $4\overline{)0}$ $4\overline{)4}$ $4\overline{)8}$ $4\overline{)12}$ $4\overline{)16}$

2. $4\overline{)20}$ $4\overline{)24}$ $4\overline{)28}$ $4\overline{)32}$ $4\overline{)36}$

3. $4\overline{)40}$ $4\overline{)44}$ $4\overline{)48}$

4. $4\overline{)24}$ $4\overline{)28}$ $4\overline{)40}$ $4\overline{)28}$ $4\overline{)24}$

5. $4\overline{)32}$ $4\overline{)24}$ $4\overline{)4}$ $4\overline{)24}$ $4\overline{)12}$

6. $4\overline{)20}$ $4\overline{)44}$ $4\overline{)32}$ $4\overline{)20}$ $4\overline{)8}$

7. $4\overline{)12}$ $4\overline{)24}$ $4\overline{)4}$ $4\overline{)24}$ $4\overline{)32}$

8. $4\overline{)8}$ $4\overline{)20}$ $4\overline{)32}$ $4\overline{)44}$ $4\overline{)20}$

9. $4\overline{)36}$ $4\overline{)32}$ $4\overline{)48}$ $4\overline{)32}$ $4\overline{)36}$

"Let the floods clap their hands." Psalm 98:8

10.  

11.   

12. The Bible says that Abraham lived for 175 years. Moses lived for 120 years. How much older was Abraham than Moses?

13. 62 apples are red and 28 are yellow. What is the sum of apples?

14. Rose is 15 years old and Ann is eight. How much younger is Ann than Rose?

15. Mother baked cookies for 26 minutes. For fourteen minutes she washed the dishes. What was the difference in the number of minutes?

1.	$4\overline{)32}$	$4\overline{)36}$	$4\overline{)20}$	$4\overline{)28}$	$4\overline{)16}$
2.	$4\overline{)24}$	$4\overline{)40}$	$4\overline{)36}$	$4\overline{)16}$	$4\overline{)28}$
3.	$4\overline{)20}$	$4\overline{)36}$	$4\overline{)32}$	$4\overline{)48}$	$4\overline{)12}$
4.	$4\overline{)36}$	$4\overline{)40}$	$4\overline{)24}$	$4\overline{)12}$	$4\overline{)48}$
5.	$4\overline{)8}$	$4\overline{)44}$	$4\overline{)4}$	$4\overline{)32}$	$4\overline{)12}$
6.	$4\overline{)16}$	$4\overline{)0}$	$4\overline{)8}$	$4\overline{)12}$	$4\overline{)32}$
7.	$4\overline{)4}$	$4\overline{)44}$	$4\overline{)8}$	$4\overline{)24}$	$4\overline{)36}$
8.	$4\overline{)8}$	$4\overline{)0}$	$4\overline{)16}$	$4\overline{)36}$	$4\overline{)24}$
9.	$4\overline{)28}$	$4\overline{)20}$	$4\overline{)4}$	$4\overline{)20}$	$4\overline{)28}$

"Let the floods clap their hands." Psalm 98:8

10. 8 nickels + 5 dimes 8 dimes + 17 pennies

11. 3 quarters + 3 nickels 2 quarters + 9 nickels

12. 6 nickels + 3 dimes 2 quarters + 7 nickels

13. 1 quarter + 5 nickels 1 quarter + 12 nickels

14.

43	55	43	52	35	13
14	23	22	24	20	26
+ 43	+ 56	+ 85	+ 87	+ 66	+ 68

15.

45	22	64	64	33	33
34	55	21	20	53	26
+ 29	+ 45	+ 79	+ 67	+ 49	+ 42

16. Norman's notebook is 12 inches long. How many feet is that? *Write the rule.*

1.	4)28	4)24	3)30	3)21	4)20
2.	3)27	4)40	3)18	4)36	4)44
3.	3)12	4)32	3)9	4)16	3)15
4.	4)48	4)12	3)24	3)36	3)33
5.	4)4	4)8	3)27	3)3	4)0
6.	3)24	4)36	3)6	4)32	4)20
7.	3)18	4)28	4)12	4)24	3)0
8.	4)16	3)9	3)21	3)12	3)15
9.	4)8	4)28	3)6	3)24	4)36

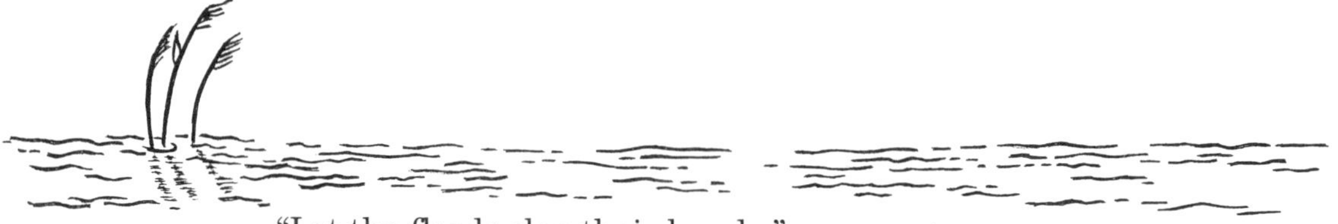

"Let the floods clap their hands." Psalm 98:8

10.  

11.   

12. 15 - 6 + 7 =   6 + 4 - 5 =

13. 9 + 6 - 8 =   13 - 6 + 6 =

14. 11 -3 + 5 =   4 + 8 - 5 =

15. 4 + 7 - 6 =   14 - 6 + 8 =

16. 14 - 5 + 8 =   14 - 7 + 8 =

17. Fred's red wagon is 3 feet long. How many yards is that? *Write the rule.*

18. The rug beside Ruth's bed is 1 yard long. How many feet is that? *Write the rule.*

1.	4)36	4)20	2)18	1)8	3)12
2.	4)40	4)28	2)12	2)8	1)7
3.	3)27	4)16	2)16	1)9	3)15
4.	3)30	2)14	4)16	4)24	3)21
5.	4)24	4)32	1)3	2)10	4)12
6.	2)2	4)4	2)20	3)36	2)4
7.	3)18	3)9	4)20	2)6	3)24
8.	1)1	1)2	4)48	1)10	3)3
9.	4)8	4)44	4)0	3)33	3)6

"Let the floods clap their hands." Psalm 98:8

10. 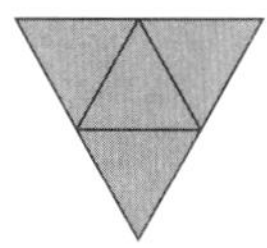  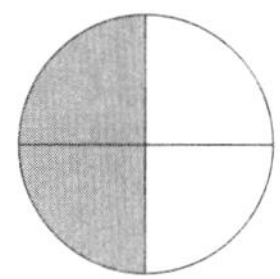 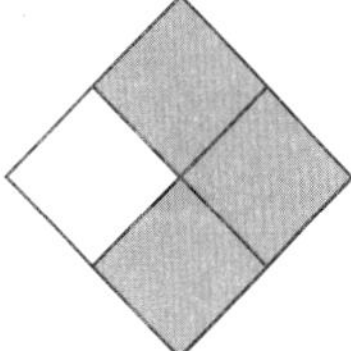

11.  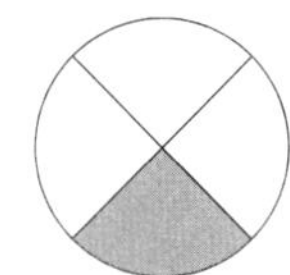 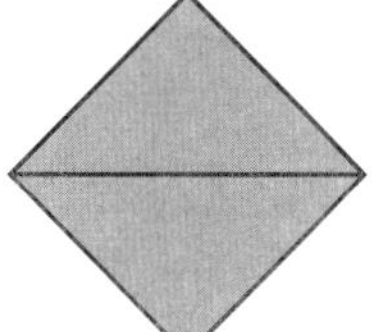 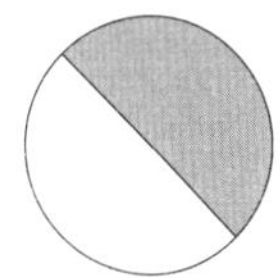

12.

603	909	960	909	803
- 327	- 668	- 358	- 256	- 186

13.

801	360	905	870	901
- 493	- 127	- 128	- 636	- 592

14.

770	708	504	902	808
- 168	- 467	- 228	- 285	- 155

15. Norma popped popcorn to treat her little brothers and sisters. The cord on the popper was 1 yard long. How many feet was that? *Write the rule.*

73

1.

0	1	2	3	4	5	6
× 5	× 5	× 5	× 5	× 5	× 5	× 5

2.

7	8	9	10	11	12
× 5	× 5	× 5	× 5	× 5	× 5

3.

9	10	6	4	2	11	8
× 5	× 5	× 5	× 5	× 5	× 5	× 5

4.

7	12	5	1	9	0	3
× 5	× 5	× 5	× 5	× 5	× 5	× 5

5.

8	11	2	4	6	10	9
× 5	× 5	× 5	× 5	× 5	× 5	× 5

6.

3	0	9	1	5	12	7
× 5	× 5	× 5	× 5	× 5	× 5	× 5

7.

8	5	7	8	5	7	6
× 5	× 5	× 5	× 5	× 5	× 5	× 5

"He weigheth the waters." Job 28:25

8. three thousand, twenty-eight

9. three thousand, seventy-three

10. two thousand, forty-six

11. two thousand, fifty-five

12. one thousand, sixty-four

13. one thousand, thirty-seven

14. three thousand, eighty-two

15.
$$\begin{array}{r} 982 \\ -\ 256 \\ \hline \end{array} \quad \begin{array}{r} 325 \\ +\ 367 \\ \hline \end{array} \quad \begin{array}{r} 790 \\ -\ 237 \\ \hline \end{array} \quad \begin{array}{r} 739 \\ -\ 397 \\ \hline \end{array} \quad \begin{array}{r} 264 \\ +\ 545 \\ \hline \end{array}$$

16.
$$\begin{array}{r} 982 \\ -\ 329 \\ \hline \end{array} \quad \begin{array}{r} 344 \\ +\ 448 \\ \hline \end{array} \quad \begin{array}{r} 991 \\ -\ 165 \\ \hline \end{array} \quad \begin{array}{r} 336 \\ +\ 573 \\ \hline \end{array} \quad \begin{array}{r} 608 \\ -\ 166 \\ \hline \end{array}$$

17. Grandmother's cane is 3 feet long. How many yards is that? *Write the rule.*

1.	7 × 5	9 × 5	6 × 5	11 × 5	3 × 5	8 × 5	2 × 5
2.	3 × 5	11 × 5	6 × 5	9 × 5	7 × 5	2 × 5	8 × 5
3.	10 × 5	12 × 5	9 × 5	8 × 5	1 × 5	4 × 5	7 × 5
4.	1 × 5	8 × 5	9 × 5	12 × 5	10 × 5	7 × 5	4 × 5

5.	32 × 4	41 × 4	62 × 3	72 × 4	90 × 4	62 × 3
6.	60 × 4	80 × 4	71 × 3	80 × 3	81 × 4	73 × 3
7.	82 × 2	64 × 2	72 × 4	93 × 2	93 ×2	90 × 4

"He weigheth the waters." Job 28:25

8.   

9.   

10. The Bible says that Joseph had 11 brothers. David had 7 brothers. How many more brothers did Joseph have than David?

11. Melvin is 23 years old. Dean is eight. How much older is Melvin than Dean?

12. Fay is twenty years old. Dawn is 9. How much younger is Dawn than Fay?

13. A starfish hunted for a clam for 120 minutes. It worked for 180 minutes to open the clam's shell. What sum of minutes was that?

1.	9×5	6×5	9×4	7×4	4×5	6×4	7×5
2.	8×5	8×4	4×4	3×5	12×5	10×5	3×4
3.	7×5	6×4	5×4	7×4	9×4	6×5	9×5
4.	3×4	10×5	12×5	3×5	4×4	8×4	8×5

5.	901×5	501×4	840×2	503×3	812×4
6.	820×3	901×3	732×3	701×4	620×4
7.	401×5	901×5	300×5	420×4	912×4

"He weigheth the waters." Job 28:25

8. $5 \times 5 + 1 =$ $\qquad$ $5 \times 6 + 1 =$

9. $3 \times 8 + 1 =$ $\qquad$ $3 \times 12 + 1 =$

10. $5 \times 7 + 1 =$ $\qquad$ $5 \times 8 + 1 =$

11. $4 \times 6 + 1 =$ $\qquad$ $4 \times 9 + 1 =$

12. $5 \times 9 + 1 =$ $\qquad$ $5 \times 10 + 1 =$

13. $2 \times 11 + 1 =$ $\qquad$ $4 \times 8 + 1 =$

14. $5 \times 11 + 1 =$ $\qquad$ $5 \times 12 + 1 =$

15. $3 \times 4 + 1 =$ $\qquad$ $4 \times 3 + 1 =$

16. Mother bought 1 pound of butter. How many ounces was that? *Write the rule.*

17. A book can weigh 16 ounces. How many pounds is that? *Write the rule.*

76

1.

9	12	8	8	7	12	5
× 5	× 4	× 5	× 4	× 5	× 3	× 4

2.

7	8	10	12	9	4	9
× 5	× 4	× 4	× 4	× 5	× 5	× 4

3.

7	9	6	12	6	3	3
× 4	× 3	× 4	× 5	× 5	× 5	× 4

4.

10	12	8	9	7	4	5
× 3	× 5	× 3	× 3	× 4	× 3	× 3

5.

601	501	923	601	712
× 4	× 5	× 3	× 5	× 4

6.

821	910	912	901	812
× 4	× 5	× 4	× 5	× 4

7.

610	932	510	801	721
× 5	× 3	× 5	× 3	× 4

"He weigheth the waters." Job 28:25

8. 4 dimes + 8 nickels

3 quarters + 24 pennies

9. 6 dimes + 6 nickels

1 quarter + 25 pennies

10. 2 quarters + 36 pennies

4 nickels + 20 pennies

11. 3 quarters + 3 nickels

1 quarter + 5 nickels

12.

22	43	61	53	54	42
54	43	23	20	33	27
+ 79	+ 84	+ 46	+ 86	+ 93	+ 96

13.

33	31	54	31	32	32
32	25	22	22	43	42
+ 35	+ 67	+ 83	+ 77	+ 58	+ 36

14. A storekeeper sold 1 pound of nuts. How many ounces was that? *Write the rule.*

1. 5×5 12×4 7×3 12×2 9×3 9×4 6×5

2. 9×3 6×4 7×3 12×4 5×5 10×3 12×3

3. 9×5 12×5 5×3 6×3 7×4 8×5 8×4

4. 7×4 9×2 3×5 12×5 9×5 8×4 10×4

5. $84 + 95$ $77 - 28$ $20 + 74$ $98 - 33$ $39 + 47$ $59 - 23$

6. $29 + 46$ $84 - 68$ $78 - 48$ $36 + 64$ $93 - 77$ $17 + 58$

7. $88 - 39$ $93 + 86$ $89 - 24$ $55 + 39$ $96 - 60$ $27 + 59$

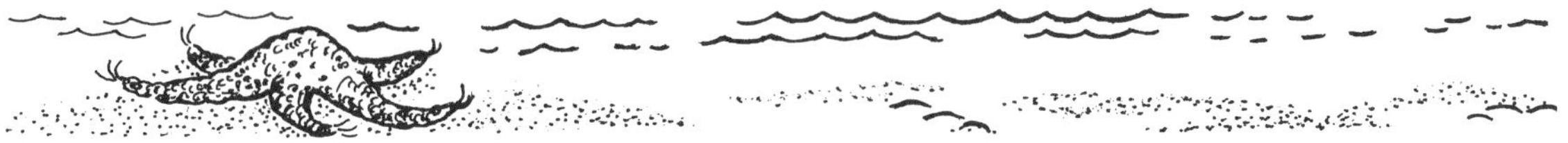

"He weigheth the waters." Job 28:25

8. 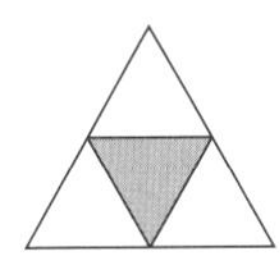 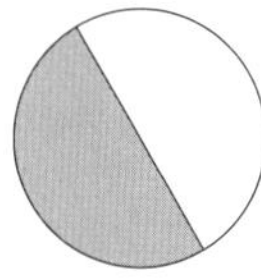 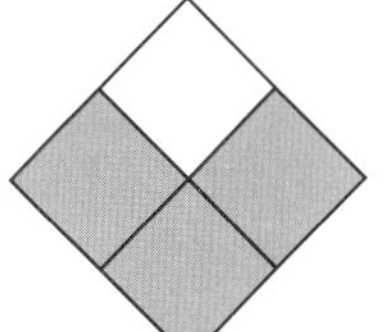 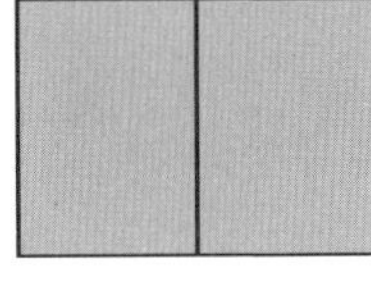

9. 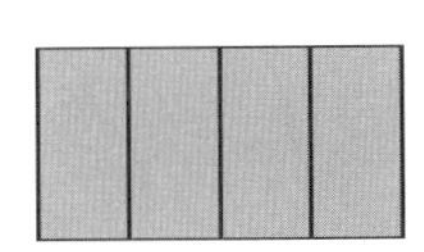 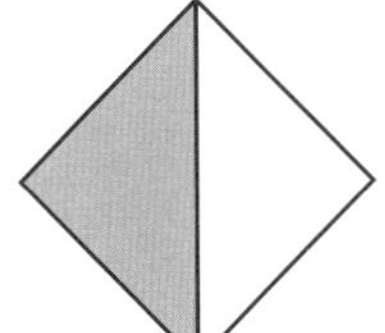 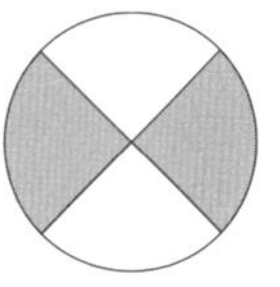 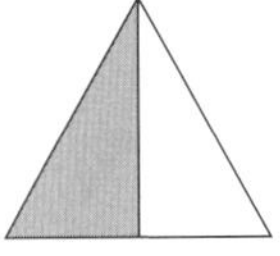

10. $2\overline{)22}$ $2\overline{)24}$ $2\overline{)12}$

11.

10. $\frac{1}{2}$ of 22 $\frac{1}{2}$ of 24 $\frac{1}{2}$ of 12

11. $\frac{1}{2}$ of 18 $\frac{1}{2}$ of 20 $\frac{1}{2}$ of 8

12. $\frac{1}{2}$ of 14 $\frac{1}{2}$ of 16 $\frac{1}{2}$ of 4

13. Mother cooked 16 ounces of fish for dinner. How many pounds was that? *Write the rule.*

1. 2×5 3×3 4×4 12×3 6×5 8×4 3×4

2. 2×4 7×4 9×3 10×4 12×5 9×5 5×3

3. 4×3 8×4 10×3 9×4 8×2 3×3 5×2

4. 3×5 9×5 12×5 8×5 9×3 7×4 4×2

5. $874 - 527$ $660 - 538$ $672 + 34$ $347 + 507$ $908 - 566$

6. $379 - 58$ $750 - 233$ $525 + 348$ $806 - 33$ $264 + 253$

7. $871 - 749$ $985 - 638$ $762 + 92$ $381 + 325$ $809 - 467$

"He weigheth the waters." Job 28:25

8.  

9.  

10. $\frac{1}{2}$ of 2 $\frac{1}{2}$ of 10 $\frac{1}{2}$ of 8

11. $\frac{1}{2}$ of 16 $\frac{1}{2}$ of 18 $\frac{1}{2}$ of 24

12. $\frac{1}{2}$ of 24 $\frac{1}{2}$ of 22 $\frac{1}{2}$ of 20

13. $\frac{1}{2}$ of 14 $\frac{1}{2}$ of 20 $\frac{1}{2}$ of 22

14. $\frac{1}{2}$ of 6 $\frac{1}{2}$ of 12 $\frac{1}{2}$ of 4

15. God made many kinds of starfish. He made a kind that can be 1 yard wide. How many feet is that? *Write the rule.*

1.	8 × 5	4 × 4	12 × 5	9 × 3	12 × 2	6 × 5	8 × 4
2.	9 × 4	6 × 3	5 × 5	0 × 1	7 × 5	7 × 3	9 × 5
3.	8 × 4	10 × 3	6 × 4	9 × 3	12 × 5	8 × 2	10 × 4
4.	9 × 5	7 × 3	7 × 5	1 × 1	5 × 5	6 × 3	12 × 3
5.	5 × 4	7 × 4	3 × 4	3 × 3	4 × 3	9 × 2	4 × 5

6.	457 + 528	906 − 581	960 − 639	390 − 25	268 + 422
7.	806 − 440	103 + 219	370 − 44	348 + 638	346 + 345

"He weigheth the waters." Job 28:25

8. $\frac{1}{2}$ of 12 $\frac{1}{2}$ of 6 $\frac{1}{2}$ of 10

9. $\frac{1}{2}$ of 16 $\frac{1}{2}$ of 8 $\frac{1}{2}$ of 14

10. $\frac{1}{2}$ of 20 $\frac{1}{2}$ of 24 $\frac{1}{2}$ of 2

11. The Bible says that Moses lived in Egypt for 40 years. He tended sheep for 40 years. He led God's people for 40 years. How many years was that in all?

12. An oak tree and a pine tree grow in the woods. The oak is 90 years old and the pine is 37. How much older is the oak than the pine?

13. Father and Jane found 6 purple starfish and nine pink starfish. What sum of starfish was that?

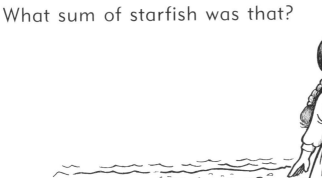

1.

3	0	10	2	8	11	8
× 5	× 5	× 2	× 5	× 4	× 4	× 2

2.

9	3	7	6	9	7	6
× 4	× 3	× 3	× 4	× 3	× 4	× 5

3.

4	11	8	5	5	0	5
× 4	× 4	× 4	× 2	× 4	× 2	× 3

4.

10	7	9	8	7	9	12
× 3	× 4	× 3	× 3	× 3	× 1	× 3

5. $4\overline{)20}$ $3\overline{)12}$ $3\overline{)3}$ $4\overline{)36}$ $2\overline{)16}$

6. $4\overline{)12}$ $3\overline{)6}$ $4\overline{)28}$ $4\overline{)24}$ $3\overline{)0}$

7. $4\overline{)32}$ $2\overline{)18}$ $4\overline{)4}$ $4\overline{)16}$ $3\overline{)15}$

8. $4\overline{)0}$ $3\overline{)18}$ $3\overline{)21}$ $4\overline{)8}$ $3\overline{)9}$

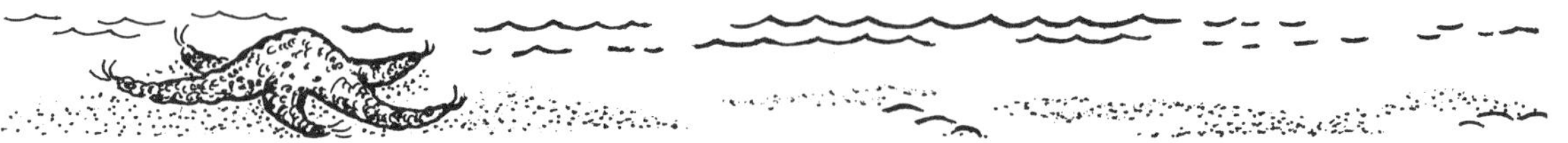

"He weigheth the waters." Job 28:25

9. 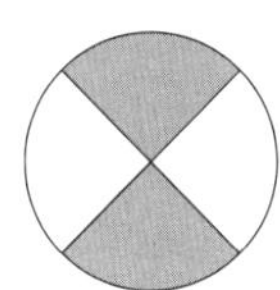 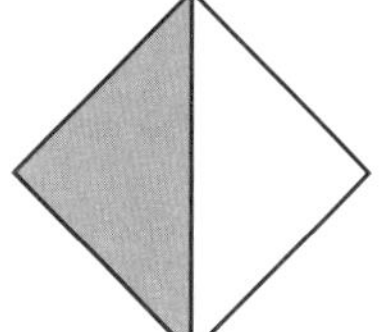 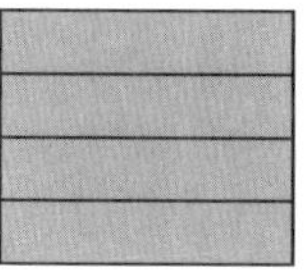

10.  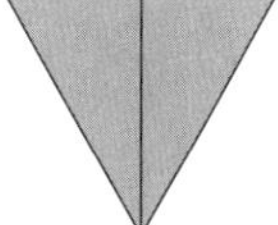 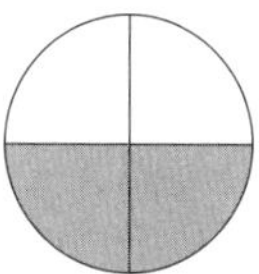

11.

  3 quarters
+ 1 nickel

  10 nickels
+ 49 pennies

12.

  2 quarters
+ 4 nickels

  8 dimes
+ 11 pennies

13.

  1 quarter
+ 7 nickels

  9 nickels
+ 3 dimes

14.

  1 quarter
+ 5 nickels

  6 dimes
+ 3 nickels

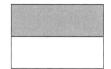

15. 16 ounces of crackers were in a box. How many pounds was that? *Write the rule.*

81

1. $5\overline{)0}$ $5\overline{)5}$ $5\overline{)10}$ $5\overline{)15}$ $5\overline{)20}$

2. $5\overline{)25}$ $5\overline{)30}$ $5\overline{)35}$ $5\overline{)40}$ $5\overline{)45}$

3. $5\overline{)50}$ $5\overline{)55}$ $5\overline{)60}$

4. $5\overline{)45}$ $5\overline{)35}$ $5\overline{)60}$ $5\overline{)40}$ $5\overline{)15}$

5. $5\overline{)60}$ $5\overline{)35}$ $5\overline{)45}$ $5\overline{)15}$ $5\overline{)40}$

6. $5\overline{)50}$ $5\overline{)10}$ $5\overline{)25}$ $5\overline{)55}$ $5\overline{)30}$

7. $5\overline{)25}$ $5\overline{)10}$ $5\overline{)50}$ $5\overline{)30}$ $5\overline{)55}$

8. $5\overline{)20}$ $5\overline{)45}$ $5\overline{)5}$ $5\overline{)0}$ $5\overline{)60}$

9. $5\overline{)5}$ $5\overline{)45}$ $5\overline{)20}$ $5\overline{)60}$ $5\overline{)0}$

"His eye seeth every precious thing." Job 28:10

10. 

11.   

12.

900	807	904	905	701
- 768	- 349	- 127	- 347	- 469

13.

904	904	500	902	903
- 258	- 339	- 379	- 237	- 157

14. Glen had 95¢ in his pocket. He found 68¢ on a store shelf and gave it to the clerk. How many more cents were in Glen's pocket than on the shelf?

15. Fay's house is 90 years old. Mark's house is 57 years old. How much older is Fay's house than Mark's?

1.	$5\overline{)40}$	$5\overline{)5}$	$5\overline{)60}$	$5\overline{)45}$	$5\overline{)25}$
2.	$5\overline{)45}$	$5\overline{)10}$	$5\overline{)40}$	$5\overline{)45}$	$5\overline{)60}$
3.	$5\overline{)25}$	$5\overline{)45}$	$5\overline{)60}$	$5\overline{)5}$	$5\overline{)40}$
4.	$5\overline{)60}$	$5\overline{)45}$	$5\overline{)40}$	$5\overline{)10}$	$5\overline{)45}$
5.	$5\overline{)50}$	$5\overline{)15}$	$5\overline{)0}$	$5\overline{)55}$	$5\overline{)35}$
6.	$5\overline{)55}$	$5\overline{)30}$	$5\overline{)20}$	$5\overline{)50}$	$5\overline{)40}$
7.	$5\overline{)35}$	$5\overline{)55}$	$5\overline{)0}$	$5\overline{)15}$	$5\overline{)50}$
8.	$5\overline{)40}$	$5\overline{)50}$	$5\overline{)20}$	$5\overline{)30}$	$5\overline{)55}$
9.	$5\overline{)35}$	$5\overline{)45}$	$5\overline{)60}$	$5\overline{)45}$	$5\overline{)35}$

"His eye seeth every precious thing." Job 28:10

10.  

11.   

12. four thousand, three hundred six

13. four thousand, one hundred forty

14. three thousand, nine hundred two

15. three thousand, seven hundred eighty

16. two thousand, five hundred six

17. one thousand, three hundred forty

18. four thousand, one hundred two

19. Mother mailed a gift to a widow. It weighed 1 pound. How many ounces was that? *Write the rule.*

1.	$5\overline{)45}$	$5\overline{)25}$	$5\overline{)10}$	$5\overline{)60}$	$5\overline{)40}$
2.	$5\overline{)25}$	$5\overline{)45}$	$5\overline{)40}$	$5\overline{)60}$	$5\overline{)10}$
3.	$5\overline{)20}$	$5\overline{)55}$	$5\overline{)35}$	$5\overline{)30}$	$5\overline{)15}$
4.	$5\overline{)35}$	$5\overline{)55}$	$5\overline{)20}$	$5\overline{)15}$	$5\overline{)30}$
5.	$5\overline{)45}$	$5\overline{)40}$	$5\overline{)55}$	$5\overline{)40}$	$5\overline{)5}$
6.	$5\overline{)40}$	$5\overline{)45}$	$5\overline{)5}$	$5\overline{)40}$	$5\overline{)55}$
7.	$5\overline{)50}$	$5\overline{)30}$	$5\overline{)0}$	$5\overline{)50}$	$5\overline{)35}$
8.	$5\overline{)0}$	$5\overline{)30}$	$5\overline{)50}$	$5\overline{)35}$	$5\overline{)50}$
9.	$5\overline{)25}$	$5\overline{)45}$	$5\overline{)60}$	$5\overline{)45}$	$5\overline{)25}$

"His eye seeth every precious thing." Job 28:10

10.

11.

12. Every verse in the Bible is from God. 31 verses are in the first chapter of the Bible. 21 verses are in the last chapter. What is the difference in the number of verses?

13. Norma set the table for company dinner. One dozen plates were for children and 19 were for parents. What was the sum of plates?

14. 158 starfish rest in the sea. 16 of the starfish are big. The rest are baby starfish.
How many are babies?

1.	$5\overline{)60}$	$5\overline{)30}$	$4\overline{)16}$	$4\overline{)8}$	$5\overline{)45}$
2.	$5\overline{)40}$	$4\overline{)20}$	$4\overline{)12}$	$5\overline{)5}$	$5\overline{)55}$
3.	$4\overline{)36}$	$5\overline{)10}$	$5\overline{)20}$	$4\overline{)24}$	$4\overline{)48}$
4.	$4\overline{)44}$	$4\overline{)4}$	$4\overline{)12}$	$5\overline{)25}$	$4\overline{)32}$
5.	$5\overline{)45}$	$4\overline{)0}$	$5\overline{)60}$	$4\overline{)36}$	$5\overline{)35}$
6.	$4\overline{)32}$	$5\overline{)40}$	$4\overline{)40}$	$5\overline{)60}$	$4\overline{)28}$
7.	$4\overline{)28}$	$5\overline{)45}$	$4\overline{)48}$	$5\overline{)0}$	$4\overline{)36}$
8.	$5\overline{)35}$	$4\overline{)48}$	$5\overline{)50}$	$4\overline{)32}$	$5\overline{)40}$
9.	$5\overline{)50}$	$4\overline{)24}$	$5\overline{)0}$	$5\overline{)30}$	$4\overline{)40}$

"His eye seeth every precious thing." Job 28:10

10.  

11.   

12. 12 - 8 + 9 = 4 + 7 - 8 =

13. 6 + 8 - 7 = 18 - 9 + 5 =

14. 17 - 9 + 6 = 7 + 6 - 6 =

15. 6 + 6 - 9 = 15 - 7 + 5 =

16. Milton's big brother was in South America for 365 days to help with a church. How many years was that? *Write the rule.*

17. A fish bit off the arm of a starfish. In 1 year a new arm grew. How many days was that? *Write the rule.*

1.	$5\overline{)40}$	$5\overline{)45}$	$3\overline{)9}$	$4\overline{)32}$	$4\overline{)40}$
2.	$5\overline{)60}$	$3\overline{)33}$	$3\overline{)6}$	$3\overline{)0}$	$4\overline{)16}$
3.	$3\overline{)30}$	$3\overline{)24}$	$5\overline{)15}$	$4\overline{)36}$	$5\overline{)40}$
4.	$5\overline{)20}$	$5\overline{)0}$	$5\overline{)10}$	$4\overline{)44}$	$5\overline{)60}$
5.	$3\overline{)15}$	$5\overline{)55}$	$4\overline{)12}$	$5\overline{)60}$	$3\overline{)12}$
6.	$5\overline{)45}$	$4\overline{)8}$	$5\overline{)45}$	$4\overline{)32}$	$5\overline{)50}$
7.	$5\overline{)20}$	$4\overline{)48}$	$5\overline{)15}$	$5\overline{)55}$	$5\overline{)25}$
8.	$5\overline{)50}$	$5\overline{)40}$	$4\overline{)36}$	$5\overline{)10}$	$3\overline{)27}$
9.	$4\overline{)48}$	$5\overline{)25}$	$3\overline{)27}$	$4\overline{)20}$	$3\overline{)36}$

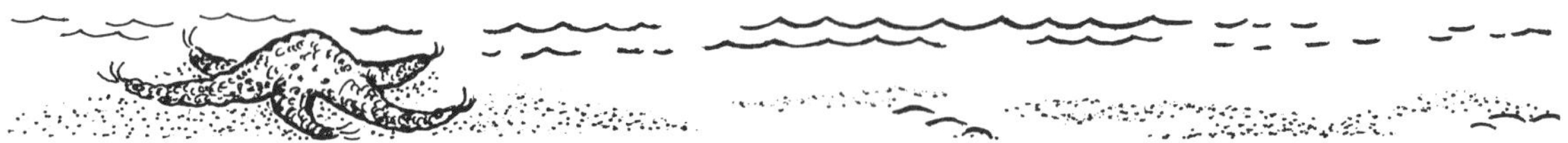

"His eye seeth every precious thing." Job 28:10

10. $5 \times 12 + 1 =$ $5 \times 7 + 1 =$

11. $5 \times 8 + 1 =$ $3 \times 10 + 1 =$

12. $5 \times 9 + 1 =$ $5 \times 10 + 1 =$

13. $4 \times 9 + 1 =$ $3 \times 12 + 1 =$

14. $2 \times 12 + 1 =$ $4 \times 0 + 1 =$

15. $3 \times 0 + 1 =$ $3 \times 8 + 1 =$

16. $5 \times 11 + 1 =$ $5 \times 0 + 1 =$

17.

36	58	72	52	32	24
22	30	22	26	57	33
+ 95	+ 93	+ 73	+ 49	+ 82	+ 87

18.

43	63	15	54	12	33
16	11	63	22	74	54
+ 84	+ 96	+ 48	+ 90	+ 94	+ 65

19. In 365 days God sends winter, spring, summer, and fall. How many years is that? *Write the rule.*

1.	5)30	5)55	4)36	5)40	3)18
2.	4)44	4)24	2)12	4)32	5)45
3.	5)50	2)18	1)10	5)0	1)9
4.	5)50	3)27	4)40	4)36	1)0
5.	4)48	5)45	3)30	4)28	3)24
6.	4)36	5)60	5)40	5)35	2)20
7.	5)20	4)48	3)36	4)32	5)30
8.	2)24	5)60	4)16	4)24	2)16
9.	2)22	3)27	3)18	2)18	3)33

"His eye seeth every precious thing." Job 28:10

10. $\begin{array}{r} 12 \text{ nickels} \\ + \ 3 \text{ dimes} \\ \hline \end{array}$ $\begin{array}{r} 3 \text{ quarters} \\ + \ 4 \text{ nickels} \\ \hline \end{array}$

11. $\begin{array}{r} 1 \text{ quarter} \\ + \ 5 \text{ nickels} \\ \hline \end{array}$ $\begin{array}{r} 3 \text{ quarters} \\ + \ 19 \text{ pennies} \\ \hline \end{array}$

12. $\begin{array}{r} 1 \text{ quarter} \\ + \ 10 \text{ nickels} \\ \hline \end{array}$ $\begin{array}{r} 7 \text{ nickels} \\ + \ 5 \text{ dimes} \\ \hline \end{array}$

13. $\begin{array}{r} 2 \text{ quarters} \\ + \ 9 \text{ nickels} \\ \hline \end{array}$ $\begin{array}{r} 1 \text{ quarter} \\ + \ 13 \text{ nickels} \\ \hline \end{array}$

14. $\frac{1}{4}$ of 32 $\frac{1}{4}$ of 36 $\frac{1}{4}$ of 48

15. $\frac{1}{4}$ of 28 $\frac{1}{4}$ of 40 $\frac{1}{4}$ of 44

16. $\frac{1}{4}$ of 24 $\frac{1}{4}$ of 20 $\frac{1}{4}$ of 16

17. The Bible says that Samuel lived at the temple. After 1 year his mother made a little coat and took it to him. How many days was that? *Write the rule.*

1.	$5\overline{)45}$	$4\overline{)28}$	$1\overline{)0}$	$5\overline{)40}$	$5\overline{)30}$
2.	$3\overline{)21}$	$5\overline{)45}$	$4\overline{)24}$	$4\overline{)32}$	$4\overline{)0}$
3.	$5\overline{)60}$	$5\overline{)25}$	$4\overline{)28}$	$3\overline{)36}$	$4\overline{)36}$
4.	$5\overline{)35}$	$3\overline{)15}$	$4\overline{)48}$	$3\overline{)27}$	$2\overline{)24}$
5.	$1\overline{)9}$	$4\overline{)32}$	$2\overline{)20}$	$3\overline{)18}$	$3\overline{)21}$
6.	$5\overline{)40}$	$2\overline{)18}$	$2\overline{)14}$	$2\overline{)12}$	$5\overline{)50}$
7.	$4\overline{)20}$	$3\overline{)12}$	$3\overline{)24}$	$4\overline{)16}$	$5\overline{)55}$
8.	$2\overline{)16}$	$2\overline{)8}$	$5\overline{)25}$	$4\overline{)44}$	$5\overline{)20}$
9.	$5\overline{)15}$	$4\overline{)48}$	$4\overline{)36}$	$5\overline{)60}$	$3\overline{)9}$

"His eye seeth every precious thing." Job 28:10

10. $5 \times 8 + 2 =$ $4 \times 6 + 2 =$

11. $5 \times 12 + 2 =$ $4 \times 11 + 2 =$

12. $5 \times 0 + 2 =$ $5 \times 9 + 2 =$

13. $4 \times 10 + 2 =$ $3 \times 8 + 2 =$

14.   

15.   

16. $\frac{1}{4}$ of 20 $\frac{1}{4}$ of 24 $\frac{1}{4}$ of 36

17. $\frac{1}{4}$ of 16 $\frac{1}{4}$ of 28 $\frac{1}{4}$ of 32

18. $\frac{1}{4}$ of 12 $\frac{1}{4}$ of 8 $\frac{1}{4}$ of 4

1. $5\overline{)45}$ $4\overline{)48}$ $5\overline{)35}$ $3\overline{)27}$ $4\overline{)24}$

2. $4\overline{)32}$ $3\overline{)36}$ $5\overline{)15}$ $4\overline{)20}$ $3\overline{)24}$

3. $5\overline{)30}$ $5\overline{)45}$ $4\overline{)28}$ $5\overline{)60}$ $4\overline{)36}$

4. $1\overline{)8}$ $5\overline{)25}$ $3\overline{)9}$ $2\overline{)24}$ $5\overline{)40}$

5. $\begin{array}{r} 12 \\ \times 5 \\ \hline \end{array}$ $\begin{array}{r} 8 \\ \times 4 \\ \hline \end{array}$ $\begin{array}{r} 7 \\ \times 5 \\ \hline \end{array}$ $\begin{array}{r} 8 \\ \times 3 \\ \hline \end{array}$ $\begin{array}{r} 12 \\ \times 4 \\ \hline \end{array}$ $\begin{array}{r} 6 \\ \times 5 \\ \hline \end{array}$ $\begin{array}{r} 10 \\ \times 4 \\ \hline \end{array}$

6. $\begin{array}{r} 9 \\ \times 5 \\ \hline \end{array}$ $\begin{array}{r} 12 \\ \times 3 \\ \hline \end{array}$ $\begin{array}{r} 7 \\ \times 4 \\ \hline \end{array}$ $\begin{array}{r} 4 \\ \times 5 \\ \hline \end{array}$ $\begin{array}{r} 9 \\ \times 5 \\ \hline \end{array}$ $\begin{array}{r} 8 \\ \times 4 \\ \hline \end{array}$ $\begin{array}{r} 9 \\ \times 4 \\ \hline \end{array}$

7. $\begin{array}{r} 8 \\ \times 5 \\ \hline \end{array}$ $\begin{array}{r} 10 \\ \times 3 \\ \hline \end{array}$ $\begin{array}{r} 12 \\ \times 4 \\ \hline \end{array}$ $\begin{array}{r} 6 \\ \times 4 \\ \hline \end{array}$ $\begin{array}{r} 7 \\ \times 5 \\ \hline \end{array}$ $\begin{array}{r} 8 \\ \times 4 \\ \hline \end{array}$ $\begin{array}{r} 12 \\ \times 5 \\ \hline \end{array}$

8. $\begin{array}{r} 9 \\ \times 4 \\ \hline \end{array}$ $\begin{array}{r} 8 \\ \times 4 \\ \hline \end{array}$ $\begin{array}{r} 9 \\ \times 5 \\ \hline \end{array}$ $\begin{array}{r} 5 \\ \times 4 \\ \hline \end{array}$ $\begin{array}{r} 7 \\ \times 4 \\ \hline \end{array}$ $\begin{array}{r} 9 \\ \times 4 \\ \hline \end{array}$ $\begin{array}{r} 9 \\ \times 5 \\ \hline \end{array}$

"His eye seeth every precious thing." Job 28:10

9. $5 \times 9 + 2 =$ $\qquad$ $4 \times 7 + 2 =$

10. $3 \times 9 + 2 =$ $\qquad$ $4 \times 11 + 2 =$

11. $3 \times 12 + 2 =$ $\qquad$ $4 \times 10 + 2 =$

12. $5 \times 8 + 2 =$ $\qquad$ $4 \times 9 + 2 =$

13. The Bible says that Moses sang. A song that he sang is 19 verses long. Another song is 43 verses long. What is the sum of verses?

14. Father's truck is seventeen years old. His car is eight years old. How much older is the truck than the car?

15. Grandfather delights in the Bible. He read 355 verses this week and 238 verses last week. How many more verses did he read this week than last week?

"The LORD on high
is mightier than...
the mighty waves
of the sea.
HOLY BIBLE

89

1.

0	1	2	3	4	5	6
× 6	× 6	× 6	× 6	× 6	× 6	× 6

2.

7	8	9	10	11	12
× 6	× 6	× 6	× 6	× 6	× 6

3.

9	10	8	2	12	6	8
× 6	× 6	× 6	× 6	× 6	× 6	× 6

4.

7	4	1	9	12	5	11
× 6	× 6	× 6	× 6	× 6	× 6	× 6

5.

8	6	12	2	8	10	9
× 6	× 6	× 6	× 6	× 6	× 6	× 6

6.

11	5	12	9	1	4	7
× 6	× 6	× 6	× 6	× 6	× 6	× 6

7.

3	8	7	0	7	8	3
× 6	× 6	× 6	× 6	× 6	× 6	× 6

"He saith to the snow, Be thou on the earth." Job 37:6

8. $\frac{1}{4}$ of 48 $\frac{1}{4}$ of 28 $\frac{1}{4}$ of 8

9. $\frac{1}{4}$ of 36 $\frac{1}{4}$ of 32 $\frac{1}{4}$ of 12

10. $\frac{1}{4}$ of 44 $\frac{1}{4}$ of 24 $\frac{1}{4}$ of 4

11. $\frac{1}{4}$ of 32 $\frac{1}{4}$ of 36 $\frac{1}{4}$ of 16

12. $\frac{1}{4}$ of 40 $\frac{1}{4}$ of 20 $\frac{1}{4}$ of 0

13. $\begin{array}{r} 897 \\ -\,539 \\ \hline \end{array}$ $\begin{array}{r} 847 \\ -\,382 \\ \hline \end{array}$ $\begin{array}{r} 603 \\ -\,483 \\ \hline \end{array}$ $\begin{array}{r} 129 \\ +\,337 \\ \hline \end{array}$ $\begin{array}{r} 788 \\ -\,429 \\ \hline \end{array}$

14. $\begin{array}{r} 509 \\ +\,289 \\ \hline \end{array}$ $\begin{array}{r} 706 \\ -\,342 \\ \hline \end{array}$ $\begin{array}{r} 443 \\ +\,264 \\ \hline \end{array}$ $\begin{array}{r} 605 \\ -\,240 \\ \hline \end{array}$ $\begin{array}{r} 907 \\ -\,109 \\ \hline \end{array}$

15. $\begin{array}{r} 393 \\ +\,465 \\ \hline \end{array}$ $\begin{array}{r} 559 \\ -\,172 \\ \hline \end{array}$ $\begin{array}{r} 700 \\ -\,689 \\ \hline \end{array}$ $\begin{array}{r} 749 \\ -\,361 \\ \hline \end{array}$ $\begin{array}{r} 275 \\ +\,584 \\ \hline \end{array}$

16. At the South Pole there is snow and ice for 365 days at a time. How many years is that? *Write the rule.*

90

1.	12 × 6	9 × 6	5 × 6	3 × 6	9 × 6	1 × 6	8 × 6
2.	9 × 6	12 × 6	8 × 6	1 × 6	9 × 6	3 × 6	5 × 6
3.	4 × 6	6 × 6	8 × 6	12 × 6	11 × 6	2 × 6	7 × 6
4.	11 × 6	12 × 6	8 × 6	6 × 6	4 × 6	7 × 6	2 × 6
5.	8 × 6	7 × 6	10 × 6	6 × 6	12 × 6	7 × 6	0 × 6
6.	7 × 6	8 × 6	0 × 6	7 × 6	12 × 6	6 × 6	10 × 6
7.	9 × 6	7 × 6	8 × 6	5 × 6	8 × 6	7 × 6	9 × 6

"He saith to the snow, Be thou on the earth." Job 37:6

8.

9.

10.

21	36	45	54	25	33
42	42	32	30	34	55
+ 97	+ 69	+ 98	+ 96	+ 89	+ 73

11.

34	64	65	23	55	53
24	20	21	66	23	34
+ 95	+ 87	+ 95	+ 87	+ 94	+ 67

12. Janet counted cups for an all-day church meeting dinner. One dozen cups were green. 54 cups were blue. 37 cups were white. How many cups was that altogether?

13. Father has a Bible that is 200 years old and a songbook that is 120 years old. How much older is the Bible than the songbook?

91

1.	10 × 6	9 × 6	8 × 6	8 × 5	4 × 6	6 × 5	11 × 6
2.	7 × 6	4 × 5	2 × 6	0 × 6	12 × 6	3 × 6	7 × 5
3.	11 × 6	5 × 6	4 × 6	8 × 5	8 × 6	9 × 6	12 × 5
4.	7 × 5	3 × 6	12 × 6	0 × 6	2 × 6	4 × 5	7 × 6
5.	6 × 6	3 × 5	1 × 6	9 × 6	7 × 6	8 × 6	10 × 5
6.	12 × 6	9 × 5	5 × 5	11 × 5	5 × 5	9 × 5	12 × 6
7.	10 × 5	8 × 6	7 × 6	9 × 6	1 × 6	3 × 5	6 × 6

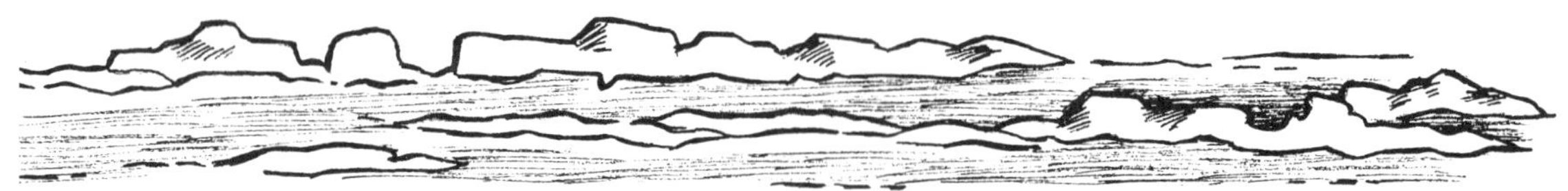

8. 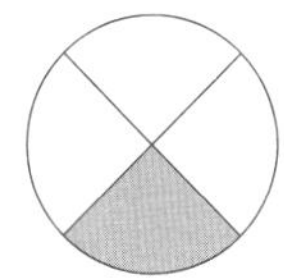 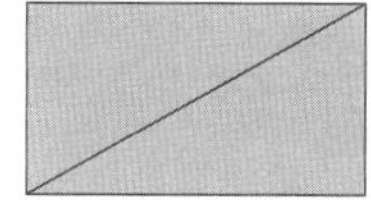 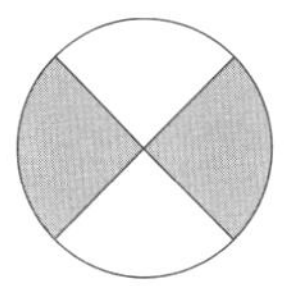 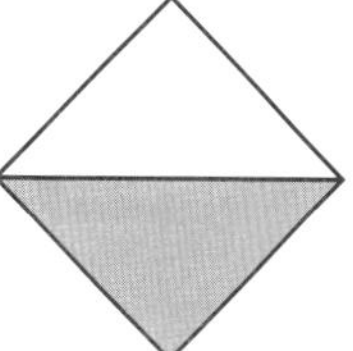

9. 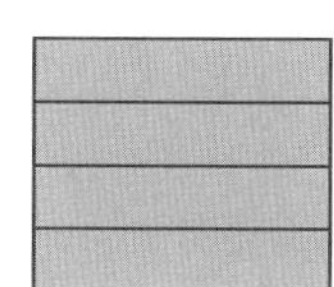 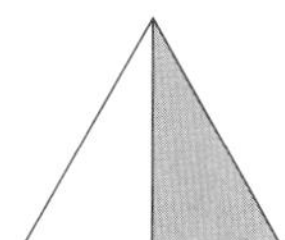 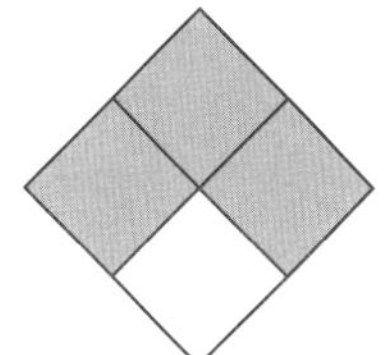 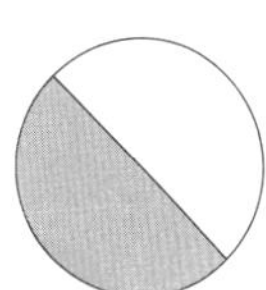

10. $5 \times 12 + 2 =$ $6 \times 8 + 2 =$

11. $4 \times 9 + 2 =$ $4 \times 6 + 2 =$

12. $3 \times 8 + 2 =$ $6 \times 6 + 2 =$

13. $4 \times 12 + 2 =$ $6 \times 10 + 2 =$

14. $6 \times 12 + 2 =$

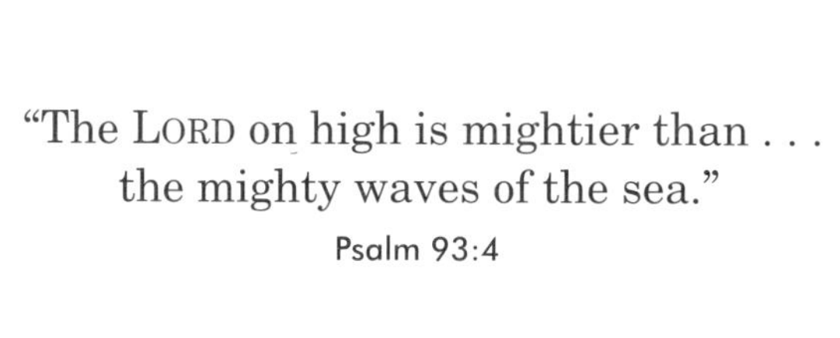

"The LORD on high is mightier than . . .
the mighty waves of the sea."
Psalm 93:4

1.	9 × 6	7 × 6	10 × 4	5 × 5	3 × 6	7 × 4	8 × 6
2.	6 × 6	11 × 6	7 × 5	4 × 6	3 × 5	4 × 4	2 × 6
3.	12 × 4	7 × 4	3 × 6	5 × 5	8 × 5	7 × 6	9 × 6
4.	2 × 6	4 × 4	3 × 5	6 × 4	7 × 5	11 × 6	9 × 4
5.	12 × 6	9 × 5	5 × 4	1 × 6	9 × 6	7 × 6	12 × 6
6.	10 × 6	5 × 6	8 × 6	0 × 6	8 × 6	6 × 5	12 × 5
7.	12 × 6	7 × 6	9 × 6	1 × 6	4 × 5	9 × 5	12 × 6

"He saith to the snow, Be thou on the earth." Job 37:6

8. 4 dimes + 10 nickels

2 quarters + 4 nickels

9. 9 nickels + 2 dimes

2 quarters + 5 nickels

10. 3 quarters + 22 pennies

1 quarter + 12 nickels

11. 6 × 12 = 6 × 9 = 4 × 8 =

12. 5 × 9 = 5 × 12 = 6 × 8 =

13. 4 × 9 = 5 × 8 = 4 × 9 =

14. 4 × 12 = 5 × 12 = 5 × 9 =

15. 4 × 8 = 6 × 9 = 6 × 12 =

16. A penguin can be 1 yard tall. How many feet is that?

Write the rule.

1.	12 × 6	6 × 6	12 × 4	9 × 6	4 × 4	8 × 6	10 × 4
2.	4 × 4	9 × 6	8 × 6	9 × 4	12 × 6	8 × 5	12 × 4
3.	10 × 6	5 × 6	9 × 6	11 × 6	0 × 6	8 × 4	3 × 6
4.	10 × 3	12 × 5	6 × 3	8 × 4	0 × 4	11 × 6	9 × 6
5.	7 × 6	9 × 5	5 × 3	7 × 5	7 × 4	4 × 5	2 × 6
6.	7 × 4	7 × 5	3 × 5	9 × 5	7 × 6	3 × 4	5 × 4
7.	12 × 3	4 × 6	7 × 6	3 × 3	12 × 6	8 × 3	6 × 6

"He saith to the snow, Be thou on the earth." Job 37:6

8.

9.

10.	6 × 9 =	5 × 12 =	3 × 8 =
11.	3 × 12 =	6 × 7 =	4 × 9 =
12.	6 × 4 =	6 × 6 =	6 × 9 =
13.	6 × 8 =	6 × 7 =	6 × 12 =
14.	6 × 12 =	6 × 10 =	4 × 12 =

15. Norman's family has a horse that is 25 years old and a cow that is sixteen years old. How much younger is the cow than the horse?

1.	4	8	9	5	12	10	8
	× 6	× 5	× 4	× 6	× 6	× 2	× 6
2.	12	10	6	12	5	12	6
	× 3	× 4	× 4	× 4	× 4	× 6	× 5
3.	7	7	4	0	8	9	12
	× 4	× 6	× 3	× 1	× 3	× 2	× 5
4.	0	2	7	7	10	3	12
	× 4	× 6	× 6	× 4	× 6	× 6	× 2
5.	7	11	7	9	9	8	8
	× 3	× 6	× 5	× 3	× 6	× 2	× 4
6.	9	7	11	7	8	4	9
	× 3	× 5	× 6	× 3	× 4	× 4	× 6
7.	3	2	4	2	2	1	0
	× 4	× 5	× 2	× 3	× 2	× 2	× 6

"He saith to the snow, Be thou on the earth." Job 37:6

8. $\frac{1}{4}$ of 4 $\frac{1}{4}$ of 20 $\frac{1}{4}$ of 8

9. $\frac{1}{4}$ of 28 $\frac{1}{4}$ of 44 $\frac{1}{4}$ of 36

10. $\frac{1}{4}$ of 48 $\frac{1}{4}$ of 32 $\frac{1}{4}$ of 40

11. A father penguin found 28 stones for a nest. The mother found 19 stones. How many more stones did the father find than the mother?

12. Fay's family sat around the table and cracked nuts. They cracked nine cups of black walnuts and $\frac{1}{2}$ dozen cups of brown walnuts. How many cups was that altogether?

13. Carl saw a stone church house that was 95 years old and a brick church house that was 58 years old. How much older was the stone church house than the brick church house?

1.	8 × 6	5 × 6	3 × 5	9 × 5	3 × 3	8 × 5	12 × 3
2.	9 × 1	9 × 5	5 × 3	6 × 5	12 × 4	9 × 4	10 × 4
3.	4 × 6	7 × 5	11 × 5	9 × 6	3 × 6	8 × 4	0 × 6
4.	7 × 5	8 × 3	0 × 5	8 × 4	9 × 2	9 × 6	11 × 5
5.	7 × 6	10 × 5	2 × 6	5 × 5	7 × 4	5 × 4	12 × 1
6.	7 × 4	5 × 5	3 × 4	10 × 5	7 × 6	4 × 3	10 × 2
7.	11 × 2	4 × 5	6 × 3	4 × 4	7 × 2	3 × 4	5 × 2

"He saith to the snow, Be thou on the earth." Job 37:6

1.
$$\begin{array}{r} 8 \\ \times\,6 \\ \hline \end{array}\qquad \begin{array}{r} 5 \\ \times\,6 \\ \hline \end{array}\qquad \begin{array}{r} 3 \\ \times\,5 \\ \hline \end{array}\qquad \begin{array}{r} 9 \\ \times\,5 \\ \hline \end{array}\qquad \begin{array}{r} 3 \\ \times\,3 \\ \hline \end{array}\qquad \begin{array}{r} 8 \\ \times\,5 \\ \hline \end{array}\qquad \begin{array}{r} 12 \\ \times\,3 \\ \hline \end{array}$$

2.
$$\begin{array}{r} 9 \\ \times\,1 \\ \hline \end{array}\qquad \begin{array}{r} 9 \\ \times\,5 \\ \hline \end{array}\qquad \begin{array}{r} 5 \\ \times\,3 \\ \hline \end{array}\qquad \begin{array}{r} 6 \\ \times\,5 \\ \hline \end{array}\qquad \begin{array}{r} 12 \\ \times\,4 \\ \hline \end{array}\qquad \begin{array}{r} 9 \\ \times\,4 \\ \hline \end{array}\qquad \begin{array}{r} 10 \\ \times\,4 \\ \hline \end{array}$$

3.
$$\begin{array}{r} 4 \\ \times\,6 \\ \hline \end{array}\qquad \begin{array}{r} 7 \\ \times\,5 \\ \hline \end{array}\qquad \begin{array}{r} 11 \\ \times\,5 \\ \hline \end{array}\qquad \begin{array}{r} 9 \\ \times\,6 \\ \hline \end{array}\qquad \begin{array}{r} 3 \\ \times\,6 \\ \hline \end{array}\qquad \begin{array}{r} 8 \\ \times\,4 \\ \hline \end{array}\qquad \begin{array}{r} 0 \\ \times\,6 \\ \hline \end{array}$$

4.
$$\begin{array}{r} 7 \\ \times\,5 \\ \hline \end{array}\qquad \begin{array}{r} 8 \\ \times\,3 \\ \hline \end{array}\qquad \begin{array}{r} 0 \\ \times\,5 \\ \hline \end{array}\qquad \begin{array}{r} 8 \\ \times\,4 \\ \hline \end{array}\qquad \begin{array}{r} 9 \\ \times\,2 \\ \hline \end{array}\qquad \begin{array}{r} 9 \\ \times\,6 \\ \hline \end{array}\qquad \begin{array}{r} 11 \\ \times\,5 \\ \hline \end{array}$$

5.
$$\begin{array}{r} 7 \\ \times\,6 \\ \hline \end{array}\qquad \begin{array}{r} 10 \\ \times\,5 \\ \hline \end{array}\qquad \begin{array}{r} 2 \\ \times\,6 \\ \hline \end{array}\qquad \begin{array}{r} 5 \\ \times\,5 \\ \hline \end{array}\qquad \begin{array}{r} 7 \\ \times\,4 \\ \hline \end{array}\qquad \begin{array}{r} 5 \\ \times\,4 \\ \hline \end{array}\qquad \begin{array}{r} 12 \\ \times\,1 \\ \hline \end{array}$$

6.
$$\begin{array}{r} 7 \\ \times\,4 \\ \hline \end{array}\qquad \begin{array}{r} 5 \\ \times\,5 \\ \hline \end{array}\qquad \begin{array}{r} 3 \\ \times\,4 \\ \hline \end{array}\qquad \begin{array}{r} 10 \\ \times\,5 \\ \hline \end{array}\qquad \begin{array}{r} 7 \\ \times\,6 \\ \hline \end{array}\qquad \begin{array}{r} 4 \\ \times\,3 \\ \hline \end{array}\qquad \begin{array}{r} 10 \\ \times\,2 \\ \hline \end{array}$$

7.
$$\begin{array}{r} 11 \\ \times\,2 \\ \hline \end{array}\qquad \begin{array}{r} 4 \\ \times\,5 \\ \hline \end{array}\qquad \begin{array}{r} 6 \\ \times\,3 \\ \hline \end{array}\qquad \begin{array}{r} 4 \\ \times\,4 \\ \hline \end{array}\qquad \begin{array}{r} 7 \\ \times\,2 \\ \hline \end{array}\qquad \begin{array}{r} 3 \\ \times\,4 \\ \hline \end{array}\qquad \begin{array}{r} 5 \\ \times\,2 \\ \hline \end{array}$$

"He saith to the snow, Be thou on the earth." Job 37:6

8. 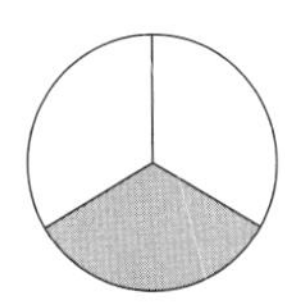 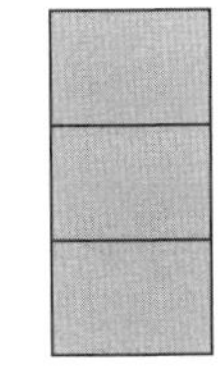 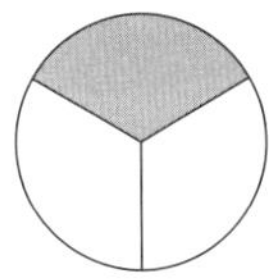 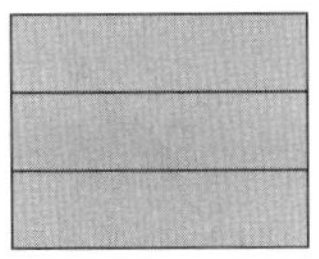

9. 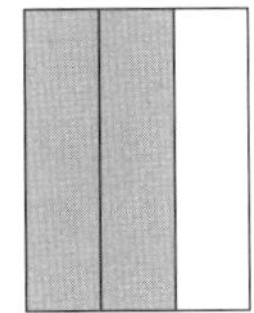 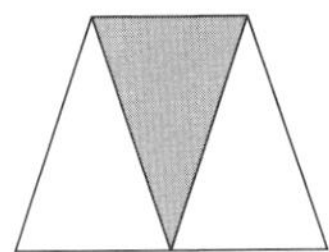 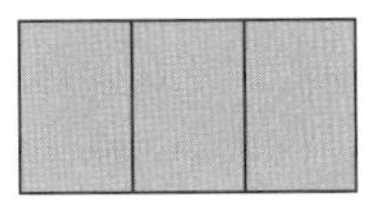 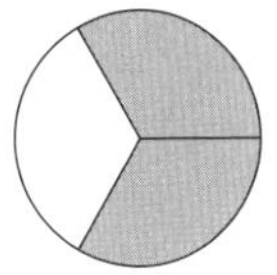

10. $4 \times 8 + 2 =$ $\qquad$ $3 \times 11 + 2 =$

11. $4 \times 9 + 2 =$ $\qquad$ $4 \times 4 + 2 =$

12. $3 \times 8 + 2 =$ $\qquad$ $2 \times 6 + 2 =$

13. $2 \times 9 + 2 =$ $\qquad$ $3 \times 6 + 2 =$

14. $2 \times 8 + 2 =$ $\qquad$ $4 \times 6 + 2 =$

15. $4 \times 3 + 2 =$ $\qquad$ $3 \times 12 + 2 =$

16. God makes the earth move around the sun in 1 year. How many days is that? *Write the rule.*

1. $5\overline{)60}$ $4\overline{)40}$ $4\overline{)32}$ $3\overline{)9}$ $4\overline{)36}$

2. $5\overline{)45}$ $4\overline{)12}$ $5\overline{)40}$ $3\overline{)30}$ $4\overline{)48}$

3. $3\overline{)27}$ $5\overline{)35}$ $4\overline{)44}$ $5\overline{)25}$ $4\overline{)24}$

4. $4\overline{)28}$ $5\overline{)45}$ $3\overline{)15}$ $5\overline{)55}$ $5\overline{)30}$

5. $5\overline{)20}$ $3\overline{)0}$ $3\overline{)21}$ $5\overline{)0}$ $4\overline{)16}$

6. 9×6 12×4 9×4 10×3 4×6 9×2 12×1

7. 3×4 3×6 12×2 5×6 12×3 8×6 9×6

8. 7×6 11×4 7×5 10×5 9×5 11×6 12×6

"He saith to the snow, Be thou on the earth." Job 37:6

9. 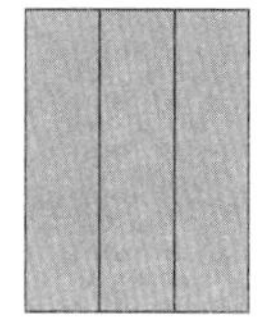 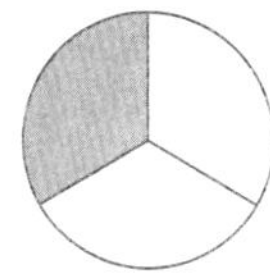 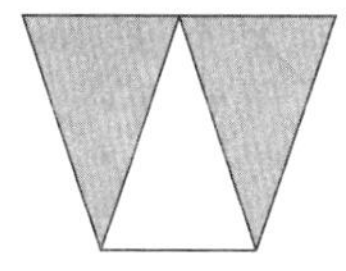 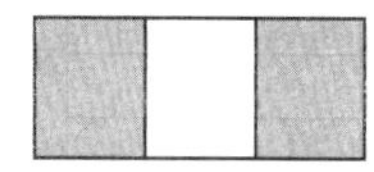

10. 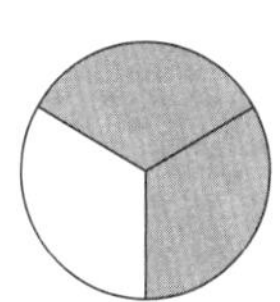 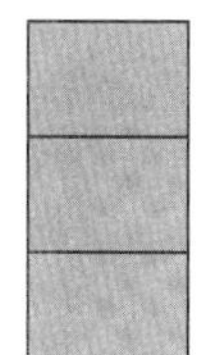 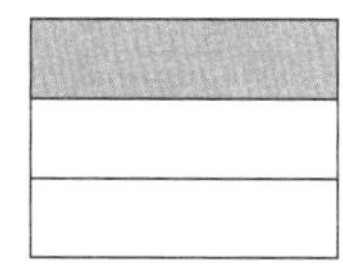 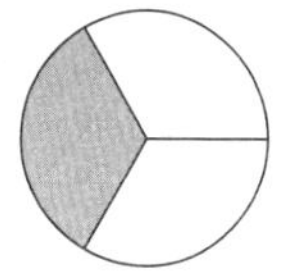

11. four thousand, two hundred ninety

12. three thousand, eight hundred seven

13. four thousand, six hundred fifty

14. three thousand, four hundred three

15. one thousand, two hundred ten

16.

$$\begin{array}{r} 586 \\ +\,869 \\ \hline \end{array} \quad \begin{array}{r} 967 \\ -\,539 \\ \hline \end{array} \quad \begin{array}{r} 775 \\ +\,598 \\ \hline \end{array} \quad \begin{array}{r} 824 \\ -\,283 \\ \hline \end{array} \quad \begin{array}{r} 704 \\ -\,336 \\ \hline \end{array}$$

17.

$$\begin{array}{r} 475 \\ +\,899 \\ \hline \end{array} \quad \begin{array}{r} 788 \\ -\,359 \\ \hline \end{array} \quad \begin{array}{r} 778 \\ +\,678 \\ \hline \end{array} \quad \begin{array}{r} 939 \\ -\,397 \\ \hline \end{array} \quad \begin{array}{r} 593 \\ -\,224 \\ \hline \end{array}$$

97

1.	$6\overline{)0}$	$6\overline{)6}$	$6\overline{)12}$	$6\overline{)18}$	$6\overline{)24}$
2.	$6\overline{)30}$	$6\overline{)36}$	$6\overline{)42}$	$6\overline{)48}$	$6\overline{)54}$
3.	$6\overline{)60}$	$6\overline{)66}$	$6\overline{)72}$		

4.	$6\overline{)48}$	$6\overline{)66}$	$6\overline{)42}$	$6\overline{)24}$	$6\overline{)12}$
5.	$6\overline{)54}$	$6\overline{)72}$	$6\overline{)36}$	$6\overline{)18}$	$6\overline{)72}$
6.	$6\overline{)12}$	$6\overline{)24}$	$6\overline{)42}$	$6\overline{)66}$	$6\overline{)48}$
7.	$6\overline{)72}$	$6\overline{)18}$	$6\overline{)36}$	$6\overline{)72}$	$6\overline{)54}$
8.	$6\overline{)60}$	$6\overline{)30}$	$6\overline{)72}$	$6\overline{)6}$	$6\overline{)0}$
9.	$6\overline{)0}$	$6\overline{)6}$	$6\overline{)72}$	$6\overline{)30}$	$6\overline{)60}$

"Who can stand before his cold?" Psalm 147:17

10. 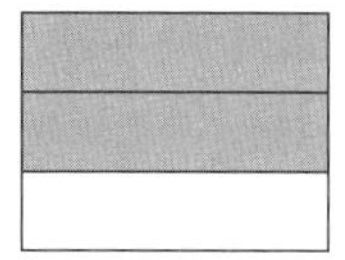 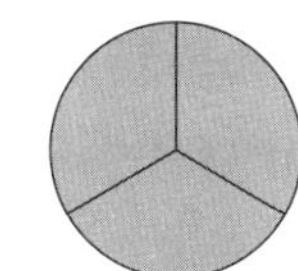 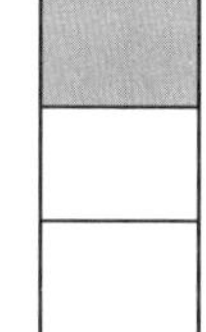 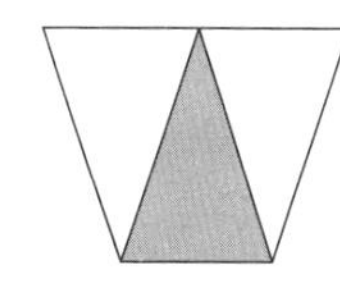

11. 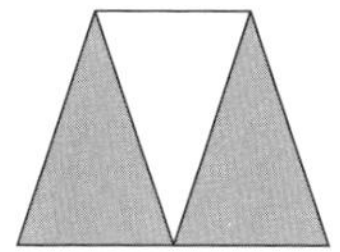 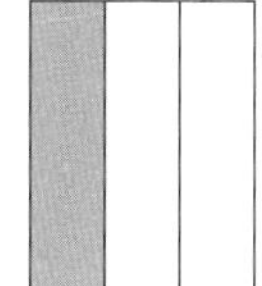 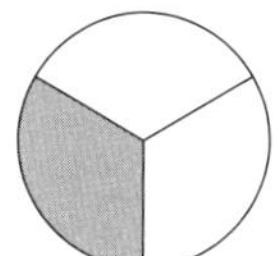 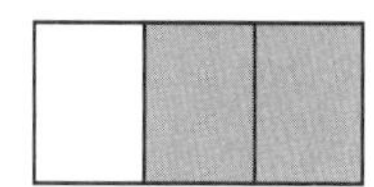

12.

900	412	802	602	613
× 4	× 4	× 3	× 2	× 3

13.

602	801	920	733	903
× 3	× 5	× 4	× 3	× 2

14.

824	600	301	401	910
× 2	× 6	× 4	× 6	× 6

15. God made a kind of penguin that can weigh 98 pounds. He made another kind that can weigh 14 pounds. What is the difference in the number of pounds?

1.	$6\overline{)42}$	$6\overline{)72}$	$6\overline{)36}$	$6\overline{)18}$	$6\overline{)54}$
2.	$6\overline{)48}$	$6\overline{)30}$	$6\overline{)12}$	$6\overline{)6}$	$6\overline{)24}$
3.	$6\overline{)54}$	$6\overline{)18}$	$6\overline{)36}$	$6\overline{)72}$	$6\overline{)42}$
4.	$6\overline{)24}$	$6\overline{)6}$	$6\overline{)12}$	$6\overline{)30}$	$6\overline{)48}$
5.	$6\overline{)60}$	$6\overline{)66}$	$6\overline{)0}$	$6\overline{)66}$	$6\overline{)60}$

6.	$4\overline{)84}$	$3\overline{)39}$	$2\overline{)62}$	$3\overline{)99}$	$2\overline{)46}$
7.	$4\overline{)80}$	$3\overline{)33}$	$2\overline{)42}$	$2\overline{)20}$	$4\overline{)48}$
8.	$3\overline{)69}$	$2\overline{)66}$	$3\overline{)93}$	$2\overline{)26}$	$3\overline{)63}$
9.	$2\overline{)24}$	$3\overline{)30}$	$3\overline{)63}$	$4\overline{)44}$	$2\overline{)40}$

"Who can stand before his cold?" Psalm 147:17

10. $\frac{1}{3}$ of 24 $\frac{1}{3}$ of 21 $\frac{1}{3}$ of 18

11. $\frac{1}{3}$ of 27 $\frac{1}{3}$ of 36 $\frac{1}{3}$ of 15

12. $\frac{1}{3}$ of 30 $\frac{1}{3}$ of 33 $\frac{1}{3}$ of 12

13. $\frac{1}{3}$ of 9 $\frac{1}{3}$ of 6 $\frac{1}{3}$ of 3

14. The Bible says that the oldest man lived 969 years. Joseph lived 110 years. What was the difference in the number of years?

15. On Sunday afternoon Ray's family sang 16 songs from *Life Songs* and 24 songs by memory. What sum of songs did they sing?

16. Penguins marched 39 miles one day and 45 miles the next. How many miles did they march on both days?

1.	$6\overline{)72}$	$6\overline{)42}$	$6\overline{)24}$	$6\overline{)12}$	$6\overline{)54}$
2.	$6\overline{)30}$	$6\overline{)18}$	$6\overline{)36}$	$6\overline{)48}$	$6\overline{)66}$
3.	$6\overline{)54}$	$6\overline{)12}$	$6\overline{)24}$	$6\overline{)42}$	$6\overline{)72}$
4.	$6\overline{)66}$	$6\overline{)48}$	$6\overline{)36}$	$6\overline{)18}$	$6\overline{)30}$
5.	$6\overline{)72}$	$6\overline{)60}$	$6\overline{)54}$	$6\overline{)6}$	$6\overline{)0}$
6.	$3\overline{)39}$	$3\overline{)96}$	$2\overline{)46}$	$4\overline{)84}$	$3\overline{)66}$
7.	$2\overline{)66}$	$4\overline{)44}$	$3\overline{)60}$	$4\overline{)84}$	$3\overline{)30}$
8.	$4\overline{)88}$	$3\overline{)63}$	$3\overline{)69}$	$2\overline{)64}$	$2\overline{)26}$
9.	$4\overline{)40}$	$2\overline{)42}$	$2\overline{)40}$	$2\overline{)22}$	$3\overline{)99}$

"Who can stand before his cold?" Psalm 147:17

10.  

11.  

12. $\frac{1}{3}$ of 12 $\frac{1}{3}$ of 9 $\frac{1}{3}$ of 6

13. $\frac{1}{3}$ of 30 $\frac{1}{3}$ of 15 $\frac{1}{3}$ of 3

14. $\frac{1}{3}$ of 27 $\frac{1}{3}$ of 18 $\frac{1}{3}$ of 0

15. $\frac{1}{3}$ of 24 $\frac{1}{3}$ of 21 $\frac{1}{3}$ of 33

16.

46	26	46	56	37	43
33	53	20	22	22	22
+ 68	+ 49	+ 73	+ 45	+ 55	+ 99

17.

16	32	33	44	32	35
43	36	24	42	43	53
+ 79	+ 59	+ 89	+ 77	+ 38	+ 34

1.	$6\overline{)48}$	$6\overline{)60}$	$6\overline{)36}$	$5\overline{)20}$	$6\overline{)72}$
2.	$5\overline{)60}$	$6\overline{)24}$	$5\overline{)30}$	$5\overline{)50}$	$5\overline{)40}$
3.	$5\overline{)45}$	$6\overline{)42}$	$5\overline{)25}$	$6\overline{)54}$	$5\overline{)40}$
4.	$5\overline{)35}$	$6\overline{)54}$	$5\overline{)45}$	$6\overline{)30}$	$6\overline{)48}$
5.	$6\overline{)18}$	$6\overline{)66}$	$6\overline{)72}$	$5\overline{)55}$	$5\overline{)15}$

6.	$4\overline{)84}$	$3\overline{)96}$	$2\overline{)46}$	$3\overline{)93}$	$4\overline{)48}$
7.	$3\overline{)36}$	$2\overline{)62}$	$3\overline{)69}$	$2\overline{)64}$	$3\overline{)63}$
8.	$4\overline{)84}$	$3\overline{)30}$	$4\overline{)44}$	$2\overline{)26}$	$4\overline{)80}$
9.	$4\overline{)40}$	$2\overline{)42}$	$3\overline{)39}$	$3\overline{)33}$	$3\overline{)60}$

"Who can stand before his cold?" Psalm 147:17

10. 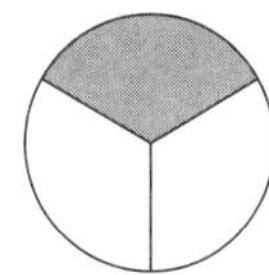 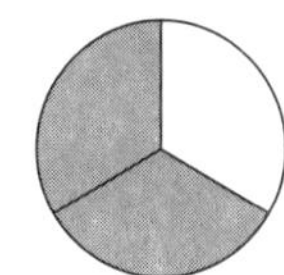 

11. 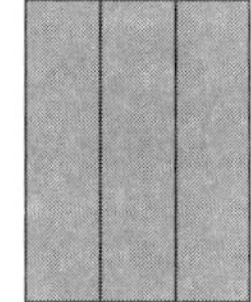 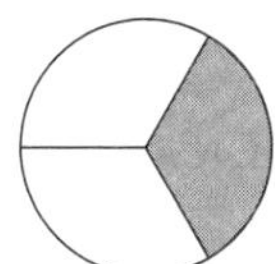 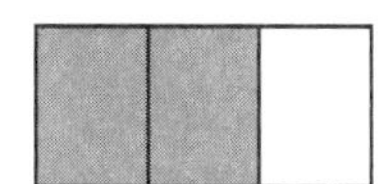 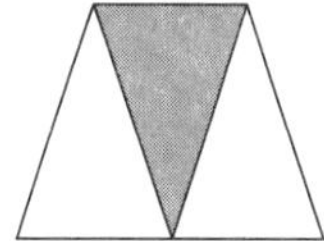

12.

3	quarters	2	quarters
+ 4	nickels	+ 7	nickels

13.

2	quarters	1	quarter
+ 6	nickels	+ 5	nickels

14.

9	nickels	8	dimes
+ 4	dimes	+ 15	pennies

15. Carl's family sang through the *Church Hymnal* in 1 year. How many days was that? *Write the rule.*

16. A penguin egg can weigh 1 pound. How many ounces is that? *Write the rule.*

1.	6)42	4)32	5)60	5)45	4)20
2.	5)25	4)36	6)72	6)48	5)35
3.	5)20	6)36	6)54	5)40	6)18
4.	5)30	6)24	6)48	6)54	5)15
5.	4)16	6)30	5)15	4)20	6)18
6.	4)8	5)0	3)9	6)0	3)6

7.	2)64	4)84	3)93	3)33	3)90
8.	2)60	4)44	2)62	3)63	3)96
9.	4)88	2)86	2)84	2)82	2)80

"Who can stand before his cold?" Psalm 147:17

10.

11.

12.

980	627	564	857	804
- 627	+ 858	+ 789	- 577	- 537

13.

865	768	358	982	359
+ 339	- 592	+ 769	- 725	+ 846

14.

787	809	557	596	779
+ 699	- 455	+ 797	- 328	- 498

15. Roy is 52 years old. Lee is 37 years old. How much younger is Lee than Roy?

16. 67 penguins climbed a snow hill. 38 of the penguins slid down the hill. How many penguins were still at the top?

1.	$6\overline{)72}$	$4\overline{)16}$	$6\overline{)24}$	$3\overline{)21}$	$6\overline{)36}$
2.	$3\overline{)12}$	$5\overline{)60}$	$4\overline{)24}$	$4\overline{)28}$	$2\overline{)8}$
3.	$2\overline{)20}$	$1\overline{)4}$	$6\overline{)60}$	$5\overline{)45}$	$3\overline{)18}$
4.	$4\overline{)40}$	$5\overline{)20}$	$5\overline{)50}$	$5\overline{)30}$	$6\overline{)54}$
5.	$3\overline{)24}$	$6\overline{)66}$	$2\overline{)24}$	$5\overline{)15}$	$6\overline{)30}$
6.	$5\overline{)55}$	$4\overline{)32}$	$5\overline{)25}$	$6\overline{)18}$	$3\overline{)36}$
7.	$6\overline{)42}$	$6\overline{)12}$	$4\overline{)48}$	$6\overline{)54}$	$5\overline{)40}$
8.	$2\overline{)24}$	$5\overline{)10}$	$5\overline{)35}$	$6\overline{)48}$	$4\overline{)36}$
9.	$6\overline{)54}$	$6\overline{)72}$	$6\overline{)0}$	$2\overline{)24}$	$4\overline{)36}$

"Who can stand before his cold?" Psalm 147:17

10.   

11.   

12. The Bible says that a king had a dream about fourteen cows. Seven of the cows were eaten up. How many cows were not eaten?

13. Mother has a cup that is 123 years old and a dish that is 108 years old. How much older is the cup than the dish?

14. Milton made a path through drifts that were 58 inches long and 49 inches long. What sum of inches was that?

1.	6)72	6)24	3)24	2)18	5)40
2.	5)20	1)12	3)27	4)32	6)48
3.	4)36	3)15	5)30	3)36	5)25
4.	6)30	6)54	5)60	6)36	4)20
5.	6)54	6)42	4)48	5)35	5)45
6.	4)8	5)0	3)9	2)0	1)2

7.	3)96	3)39	3)66	4)84	2)62
8.	2)26	2)64	3)63	4)88	3)93
9.	2)22	3)60	2)88	4)80	3)33

"Who can stand before his cold?" Psalm 147:17

10.  

11.   

12. $6 \times 8 + 2 =$ $\qquad$ $6 \times 5 + 2 =$

13. $6 \times 6 + 2 =$ $\qquad$ $5 \times 12 + 2 =$

14. $6 \times 10 + 2 =$ $\qquad$ $4 \times 9 + 2 =$

15. $5 \times 6 + 2 =$ $\qquad$ $4 \times 12 + 2 =$

16. $6 \times 9 + 2 =$ $\qquad$ $5 \times 11 + 2 =$

17. $6 \times 7 + 2 =$ $\qquad$ $4 \times 11 + 2 =$

18. Mother made baby Jane a new dress from 3 feet of cloth. How many yards was that? *Write the rule.*

104

1. $6\overline{)36}$ $4\overline{)32}$ $5\overline{)45}$ $6\overline{)60}$ $4\overline{)20}$

2. $4\overline{)48}$ $3\overline{)21}$ $4\overline{)16}$ $6\overline{)30}$ $4\overline{)36}$

3. $5\overline{)25}$ $5\overline{)50}$ $6\overline{)54}$ $3\overline{)24}$ $5\overline{)30}$

4. $5\overline{)45}$ $3\overline{)15}$ $6\overline{)24}$ $4\overline{)28}$ $3\overline{)36}$

5. $6\overline{)72}$ $5\overline{)35}$ $6\overline{)54}$ $4\overline{)44}$ $4\overline{)24}$

6. $5\overline{)55}$ $1\overline{)8}$ $2\overline{)0}$ $5\overline{)20}$ $6\overline{)18}$

7. $3\overline{)18}$ $3\overline{)33}$ $3\overline{)27}$ $6\overline{)42}$ $5\overline{)60}$

8. $5\overline{)15}$ $3\overline{)12}$ $6\overline{)0}$ $6\overline{)48}$ $6\overline{)66}$

9. $6\overline{)12}$ $3\overline{)9}$ $6\overline{)60}$ $4\overline{)12}$ $5\overline{)10}$

"Who can stand before his cold?" Psalm 147:17

Write the Roman numerals.

10. 5 3 4 2

11. 1 4 3 5

12. 6 × 8 = 6 × 9 = 5 × 11 =

13. 5 × 8 = 6 × 10 = 6 × 7 =

14. 4 × 9 = 6 × 2 = 4 × 3 =

15. 6 × 0 = 6 × 7 = 5 × 12 =

16. 6 × 6 = 6 × 11 = 6 × 9 =

17. 4 × 10 = 5 × 3 = 4 × 4 =

18. God gives snow like wool. Roy delights to catch the flakes. He caught 58 flakes on his sleeve and 46 flakes on his mitten. How many flakes was that altogether?

1.	0 × 7	1 × 7	2 × 7	3 × 7	4 × 7	5 × 7	6 × 7
2.	7 × 7	8 × 7	9 × 7	10 × 7	11 × 7	12 × 7	
3.	9 × 7	7 × 7	4 × 7	6 × 7	3 × 7	1 × 7	12 × 7
4.	11 × 7	4 × 7	7 × 7	1 × 7	3 × 7	6 × 7	8 × 7
5.	9 × 7	10 × 7	2 × 7	0 × 7	5 × 7	9 × 7	12 × 7
6.	11 × 7	0 × 7	2 × 7	10 × 7	9 × 7	5 × 7	8 × 7
7.	8 × 7	7 × 7	9 × 7	12 × 7	9 × 7	7 × 7	8 × 7

"He commanded, and they were created." Psalm 148:5

Write the Roman numerals.

8. 3 5 1 4

9. 5 3 4 2

10.

11.

12.

998	378	549	976	868
- 859	+ 689	- 76	- 737	+ 88

13.

684	964	893	796	980
- 35	+ 408	- 244	+ 576	- 276

14.

269	587	865	858	357
+ 798	- 448	- 626	- 385	+ 599

1.	$\begin{array}{r} 8 \\ \times 7 \\ \hline \end{array}$	$\begin{array}{r} 12 \\ \times 7 \\ \hline \end{array}$	$\begin{array}{r} 7 \\ \times 7 \\ \hline \end{array}$	$\begin{array}{r} 4 \\ \times 7 \\ \hline \end{array}$	$\begin{array}{r} 0 \\ \times 7 \\ \hline \end{array}$	$\begin{array}{r} 8 \\ \times 7 \\ \hline \end{array}$	$\begin{array}{r} 9 \\ \times 7 \\ \hline \end{array}$
2.	$\begin{array}{r} 3 \\ \times 7 \\ \hline \end{array}$	$\begin{array}{r} 8 \\ \times 7 \\ \hline \end{array}$	$\begin{array}{r} 0 \\ \times 7 \\ \hline \end{array}$	$\begin{array}{r} 4 \\ \times 7 \\ \hline \end{array}$	$\begin{array}{r} 7 \\ \times 7 \\ \hline \end{array}$	$\begin{array}{r} 12 \\ \times 7 \\ \hline \end{array}$	$\begin{array}{r} 11 \\ \times 7 \\ \hline \end{array}$
3.	$\begin{array}{r} 8 \\ \times 7 \\ \hline \end{array}$	$\begin{array}{r} 10 \\ \times 7 \\ \hline \end{array}$	$\begin{array}{r} 6 \\ \times 7 \\ \hline \end{array}$	$\begin{array}{r} 9 \\ \times 7 \\ \hline \end{array}$	$\begin{array}{r} 12 \\ \times 7 \\ \hline \end{array}$	$\begin{array}{r} 8 \\ \times 7 \\ \hline \end{array}$	$\begin{array}{r} 9 \\ \times 7 \\ \hline \end{array}$
4.	$\begin{array}{r} 3 \\ \times 7 \\ \hline \end{array}$	$\begin{array}{r} 8 \\ \times 7 \\ \hline \end{array}$	$\begin{array}{r} 12 \\ \times 7 \\ \hline \end{array}$	$\begin{array}{r} 9 \\ \times 7 \\ \hline \end{array}$	$\begin{array}{r} 6 \\ \times 7 \\ \hline \end{array}$	$\begin{array}{r} 10 \\ \times 7 \\ \hline \end{array}$	$\begin{array}{r} 11 \\ \times 7 \\ \hline \end{array}$
5.	$\begin{array}{r} 5 \\ \times 7 \\ \hline \end{array}$	$\begin{array}{r} 2 \\ \times 7 \\ \hline \end{array}$	$\begin{array}{r} 6 \\ \times 7 \\ \hline \end{array}$	$\begin{array}{r} 5 \\ \times 7 \\ \hline \end{array}$	$\begin{array}{r} 2 \\ \times 7 \\ \hline \end{array}$	$\begin{array}{r} 6 \\ \times 7 \\ \hline \end{array}$	$\begin{array}{r} 1 \\ \times 7 \\ \hline \end{array}$

6.	$\begin{array}{r} \$7.64 \\ -\ 2.22 \\ \hline \end{array}$	$\begin{array}{r} \$3.34 \\ +\ 5.64 \\ \hline \end{array}$	$\begin{array}{r} \$9.78 \\ -\ 3.55 \\ \hline \end{array}$	$\begin{array}{r} \$5.32 \\ +\ 4.35 \\ \hline \end{array}$
7.	$\begin{array}{r} \$3.46 \\ +\ 4.52 \\ \hline \end{array}$	$\begin{array}{r} \$7.89 \\ -\ 3.47 \\ \hline \end{array}$	$\begin{array}{r} \$2.23 \\ +\ 6.44 \\ \hline \end{array}$	$\begin{array}{r} \$8.56 \\ -\ 3.33 \\ \hline \end{array}$

"He commanded, and they were created." Psalm 148:5

Write the Roman numerals.

8. 5 3 4 1

9. 2 4 3 5

10. The Bible says that Abraham was Isaac's father. When Abraham was 123 years old, Isaac was 23 years old. How much younger was Isaac than his father?

11. Roy's minister is 54 years old, and Roy is 9. How much older is the minister than Roy?

12. Fay's family made one dozen apple pies, 24 cherry pies, and $\frac{1}{2}$ dozen peach pies. How many pies was that in all?

13. Mighty waves swept 58 sea horses through the sea. 29 of them clung to sea grass. How many did not cling to grass?

1.

9	6	5	12	5	6	9
× 7	× 7	× 7	× 7	× 7	× 7	× 7

2.

8	12	4	2	9	11	1
× 7	× 7	× 7	× 7	× 7	× 7	× 7

3.

10	7	3	0	8	7	9
× 7	× 7	× 7	× 7	× 7	× 7	× 7

4.

1	11	9	2	4	12	8
× 7	× 7	× 7	× 7	× 7	× 7	× 7

5.

9	7	8	0	3	7	10
× 7	× 7	× 7	× 7	× 7	× 7	× 7

6.

\$9.63	\$9.99	\$9.84	\$6.44
+ .35	− 2.64	− 5.63	+ 3.35

7.

\$5.25	\$6.96	\$9.78	\$8.76
+ 3.54	− 3.75	− 3.43	+ .22

"He commanded, and they were created." Psalm 148:5

8. five thousand, thirty-eight

9. three thousand, sixty-five

10. five thousand, seventy-four

11. four thousand, twenty-nine

12.	$6 \times 9 + 2 =$	$7 \times 7 + 2 =$
13.	$5 \times 7 + 2 =$	$7 \times 6 + 2 =$
14.	$6 \times 7 + 2 =$	$4 \times 9 + 2 =$
15.	$6 \times 8 + 2 =$	$5 \times 11 + 2 =$

16. In Jane's classroom there are 4 desks in each row. There are 3 rows. How many desks is that in all?

17. When Mother made buns, she put 8 buns in each pan. There were 6 pans. How many buns was that in all?

108

1.	6 × 7	12 × 7	8 × 7	9 × 6	4 × 7	8 × 6	0 × 7
2.	9 × 7	3 × 7	12 × 6	7 × 7	9 × 7	11 × 7	8 × 7
3.	9 × 6	10 × 7	5 × 7	6 × 6	5 × 7	10 × 7	9 × 6
4.	8 × 7	11 × 7	9 × 7	7 × 7	12 × 6	3 × 7	9 × 7
5.	0 × 6	8 × 6	4 × 7	9 × 6	8 × 7	12 × 7	7 × 6

6.	\$8.75 − .43	\$4.47 + 3.29	\$3.59 − .45	\$7.25 + 2.39
7.	\$4.38 + 2.38	\$7.66 − .34	\$9.88 − 1.24	\$6.64 − 4.50

"He commanded, and they were created." Psalm 148:5

8. 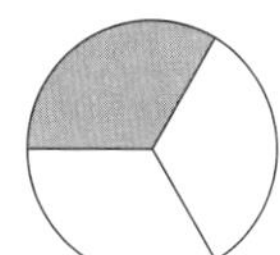  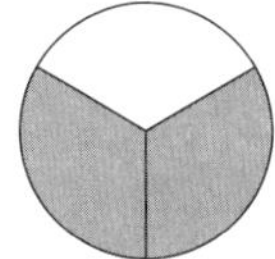 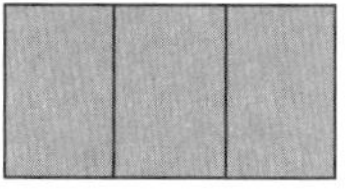

9.  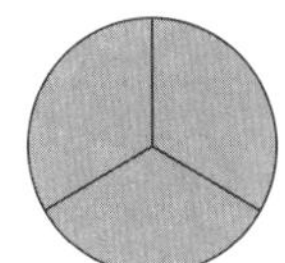 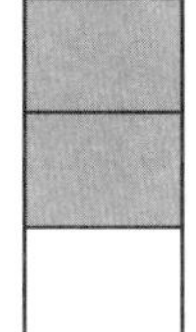 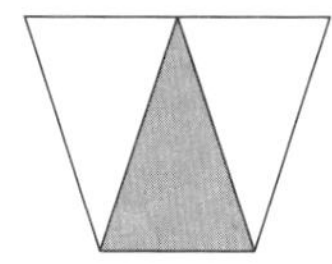

10. $\frac{1}{3}$ of 30 $\frac{1}{3}$ of 33 $\frac{1}{3}$ of 27

11. $\frac{1}{3}$ of 24 $\frac{1}{3}$ of 36 $\frac{1}{3}$ of 21

12. $\frac{1}{3}$ of 18 $\frac{1}{3}$ of 3 $\frac{1}{3}$ of 15

13. $\frac{1}{3}$ of 12 $\frac{1}{3}$ of 6 $\frac{1}{3}$ of 12

14. Ray's Sunday school teacher hung 5 charts in each row. She made 2 rows. How many charts was that altogether?

15. Father's bookcase has 12 books on each shelf. There are 6 shelves. How many books is that altogether?

109

1. 8×7 10×6 12×7 9×6 8×6 9×5 6×7

2. 12×5 8×7 9×5 8×6 9×6 12×7 7×6

3. 7×5 9×7 7×7 4×7 10×7 6×6 5×6

4. 5×7 10×7 4×7 7×7 9×7 6×5 6×6

5. $4\overline{)84}$ $3\overline{)36}$ $3\overline{)96}$ $3\overline{)90}$ $4\overline{)80}$

6. $4\overline{)88}$ $3\overline{)33}$ $3\overline{)93}$ $4\overline{)40}$ $2\overline{)42}$

7. $3\overline{)63}$ $2\overline{)60}$ $2\overline{)64}$ $4\overline{)48}$ $3\overline{)60}$

8. $3\overline{)66}$ $2\overline{)20}$ $2\overline{)62}$ $4\overline{)44}$ $4\overline{)84}$

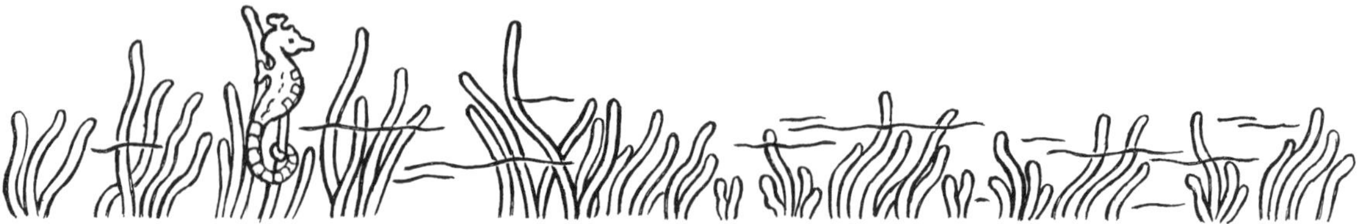

"He commanded, and they were created." Psalm 148:5

9. 

10.   

11.

$\begin{array}{r} 601 \\ \times\ 7 \\ \hline \end{array}$	$\begin{array}{r} 423 \\ \times\ 3 \\ \hline \end{array}$	$\begin{array}{r} 510 \\ \times\ 6 \\ \hline \end{array}$	$\begin{array}{r} 602 \\ \times\ 3 \\ \hline \end{array}$	$\begin{array}{r} 311 \\ \times\ 7 \\ \hline \end{array}$

12.

$\begin{array}{r} 833 \\ \times\ 3 \\ \hline \end{array}$	$\begin{array}{r} 942 \\ \times\ 2 \\ \hline \end{array}$	$\begin{array}{r} 932 \\ \times\ 3 \\ \hline \end{array}$	$\begin{array}{r} 920 \\ \times\ 4 \\ \hline \end{array}$	$\begin{array}{r} 901 \\ \times\ 6 \\ \hline \end{array}$

13.

$\begin{array}{r} 630 \\ \times\ 2 \\ \hline \end{array}$	$\begin{array}{r} 701 \\ \times\ 6 \\ \hline \end{array}$	$\begin{array}{r} 301 \\ \times\ 6 \\ \hline \end{array}$	$\begin{array}{r} 610 \\ \times\ 5 \\ \hline \end{array}$	$\begin{array}{r} 722 \\ \times\ 3 \\ \hline \end{array}$

14. The Bible says that Daniel knelt to pray 3 times each day. How many times did he pray in 7 days?

15. Joy saw 7 birds at each bird feeder. There were 4 feeders. How many birds did Joy see?

110

1. 9×7 9×6 12×4 9×5 10×4 5×7 12×7

2. 8×4 7×6 12×6 5×6 7×7 9×4 8×7

3. 9×7 7×5 8×5 9×5 8×6 9×6 12×7

4. 8×4 6×6 7×7 6×5 12×6 6×7 8×7

5. $4\overline{)48}$ $3\overline{)63}$ $4\overline{)80}$ $3\overline{)96}$ $3\overline{)90}$

6. $2\overline{)80}$ $2\overline{)84}$ $2\overline{)88}$ $2\overline{)86}$ $2\overline{)82}$

7. $2\overline{)60}$ $2\overline{)64}$ $3\overline{)60}$ $4\overline{)84}$ $2\overline{)24}$

8. $4\overline{)40}$ $3\overline{)39}$ $2\overline{)24}$ $2\overline{)26}$ $3\overline{)30}$

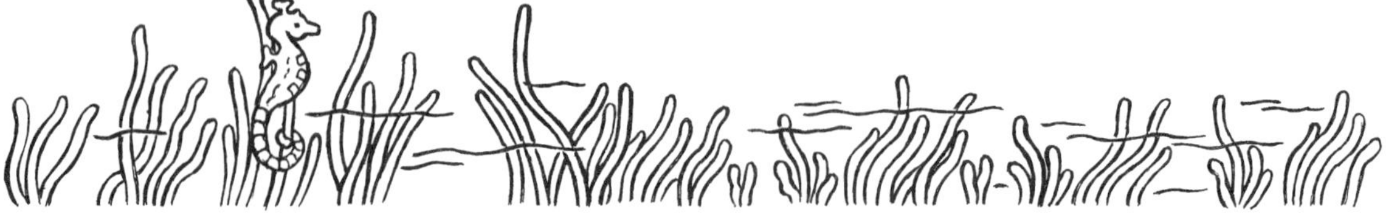

"He commanded, and they were created." Psalm 148:5

9.

5 dimes + 10 nickels	4 quarters + 5 nickels

10.

3 quarters + 7 nickels	10 dimes + 9 nickels

11.

4 quarters + 8 dimes	2 quarters + 10 nickels

12. 2 sea horses hid in each clump of sea grass. There were 7 clumps. How many sea horses was that in all?

13. Jay made a Bible verse book. He wrote 4 verses on each page. There were 7 pages. How many verses were in the book?

14. Mother put 11 grapes in each lunch. She packed 5 lunches. How many grapes did she pack altogether?

1.	6×7	8×6	10×4	7×6	12×4	8×5	9×5
2.	12×3	5×7	5×6	7×7	10×3	7×5	9×4
3.	7×4	11×7	9×6	8×4	10×7	8×3	4×4
4.	9×2	12×7	8×7	12×6	12×2	9×3	9×1
5.	3×3	9×3	4×6	12×6	8×7	12×7	6×3
6.	8×2	6×4	10×7	8×4	9×6	11×7	4×7
7.	8×6	9×7	8×7	6×6	8×7	9×7	12×4

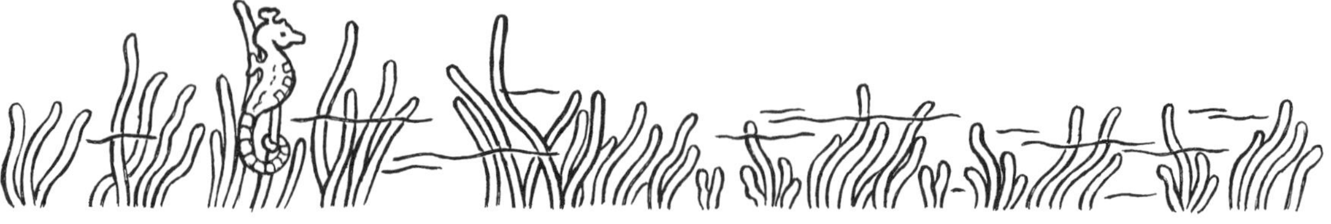

"He commanded, and they were created." Psalm 148:5

Write the Roman numerals.

8. 6 8 10 9

9. 8 7 9 10

10.

24	24	52	34	54	33
32	24	40	53	25	46
+ 58	+ 53	+ 95	+ 58	+ 97	+ 98

11.

55	31	53	12	55	45
22	56	34	26	24	33
+ 67	+ 99	+ 13	+ 75	+ 97	+ 97

12. We do not know what will happen in 1 year, but God knows. How many days is that? *Write the rule.*

13. Mother bought 1 pound of cheese. How many ounces was that? *Write the rule.*

14. Glen's little brother is 3 feet tall. How many yards is that? *Write the rule.*

1. $\begin{array}{r} 11 \\ \times 7 \\ \hline \end{array}$ $\begin{array}{r} 9 \\ \times 7 \\ \hline \end{array}$ $\begin{array}{r} 10 \\ \times 2 \\ \hline \end{array}$ $\begin{array}{r} 9 \\ \times 6 \\ \hline \end{array}$ $\begin{array}{r} 12 \\ \times 7 \\ \hline \end{array}$ $\begin{array}{r} 7 \\ \times 6 \\ \hline \end{array}$ $\begin{array}{r} 9 \\ \times 4 \\ \hline \end{array}$

2. $\begin{array}{r} 4 \\ \times 3 \\ \hline \end{array}$ $\begin{array}{r} 8 \\ \times 7 \\ \hline \end{array}$ $\begin{array}{r} 8 \\ \times 4 \\ \hline \end{array}$ $\begin{array}{r} 12 \\ \times 4 \\ \hline \end{array}$ $\begin{array}{r} 8 \\ \times 2 \\ \hline \end{array}$ $\begin{array}{r} 6 \\ \times 6 \\ \hline \end{array}$ $\begin{array}{r} 6 \\ \times 7 \\ \hline \end{array}$

3. $\begin{array}{r} 4 \\ \times 6 \\ \hline \end{array}$ $\begin{array}{r} 10 \\ \times 4 \\ \hline \end{array}$ $\begin{array}{r} 4 \\ \times 4 \\ \hline \end{array}$ $\begin{array}{r} 8 \\ \times 6 \\ \hline \end{array}$ $\begin{array}{r} 8 \\ \times 4 \\ \hline \end{array}$ $\begin{array}{r} 8 \\ \times 7 \\ \hline \end{array}$ $\begin{array}{r} 3 \\ \times 4 \\ \hline \end{array}$

4. $\begin{array}{r} 8 \\ \times 5 \\ \hline \end{array}$ $\begin{array}{r} 8 \\ \times 3 \\ \hline \end{array}$ $\begin{array}{r} 12 \\ \times 7 \\ \hline \end{array}$ $\begin{array}{r} 9 \\ \times 6 \\ \hline \end{array}$ $\begin{array}{r} 4 \\ \times 5 \\ \hline \end{array}$ $\begin{array}{r} 9 \\ \times 7 \\ \hline \end{array}$ $\begin{array}{r} 10 \\ \times 7 \\ \hline \end{array}$

5. $6\overline{)60}$ $6\overline{)42}$ $5\overline{)25}$ $6\overline{)72}$ $4\overline{)24}$

6. $5\overline{)40}$ $6\overline{)24}$ $3\overline{)24}$ $6\overline{)36}$ $5\overline{)60}$

7. $6\overline{)54}$ $6\overline{)18}$ $4\overline{)32}$ $4\overline{)16}$ $6\overline{)48}$

8. $4\overline{)12}$ $5\overline{)45}$ $6\overline{)30}$ $4\overline{)28}$ $5\overline{)50}$

"He commanded, and they were created." Psalm 148:5

Write the Roman numerals.

9. 10 8 6 9

10. 8 10 9 7

11.

\$9.89	\$5.86	\$3.69	\$8.90
- 5.67	- 3.28	+ 5.58	- 5.27

12.

\$2.73	\$6.96	\$9.49	\$7.90
+ 3.87	- 5.64	+ 9.36	- 1.29

13.

\$9.89	\$5.44	\$7.84	\$7.67
- 6.27	+ 3.82	- 5.27	- 3.46

14. Norman read 3 chapters in the Bible each day. How many chapters did he read in 6 days?

15. Jean put 53 plums in a dish. The family ate 28 of them. How many plums were left?

113

1.	$7\overline{)0}$	$7\overline{)7}$	$7\overline{)14}$	$7\overline{)21}$	$7\overline{)28}$
2.	$7\overline{)35}$	$7\overline{)42}$	$7\overline{)49}$	$7\overline{)56}$	$7\overline{)63}$
3.	$7\overline{)70}$	$7\overline{)77}$	$7\overline{)84}$		

4.	$7\overline{)70}$	$7\overline{)42}$	$7\overline{)63}$	$7\overline{)35}$	$7\overline{)49}$
5.	$7\overline{)42}$	$7\overline{)70}$	$7\overline{)49}$	$7\overline{)35}$	$7\overline{)63}$
6.	$7\overline{)84}$	$7\overline{)14}$	$7\overline{)21}$	$7\overline{)28}$	$7\overline{)77}$
7.	$7\overline{)21}$	$7\overline{)14}$	$7\overline{)84}$	$7\overline{)77}$	$7\overline{)28}$
8.	$7\overline{)56}$	$7\overline{)7}$	$7\overline{)63}$	$7\overline{)49}$	$7\overline{)56}$
9.	$7\overline{)0}$	$7\overline{)56}$	$7\overline{)56}$	$7\overline{)42}$	$7\overline{)63}$

"Praise him for his mighty acts." Psalm 150:2

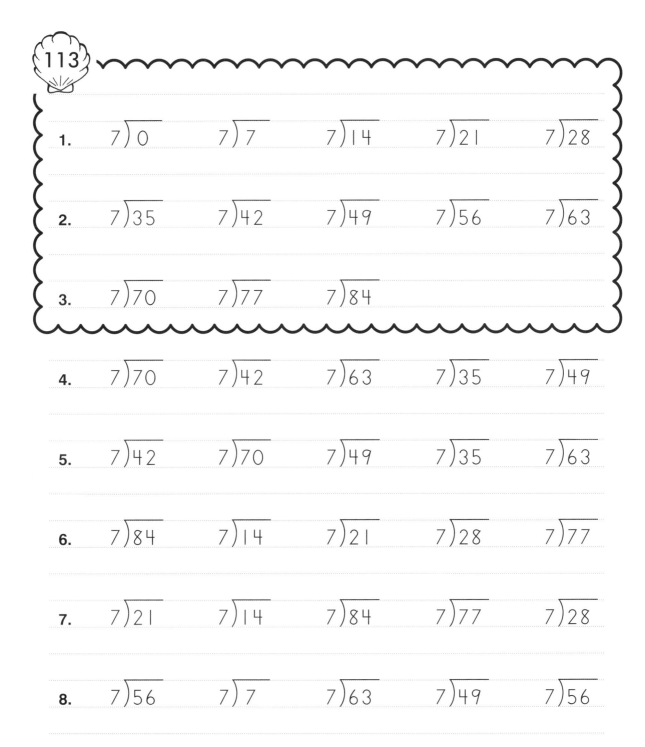

Write the Roman numerals.

10. 9 8 10 7

11. 6 10 8 9

12.

4 quarters + 100 pennies	2 quarters + 50 pennies

13.

3 quarters + 12 nickels	4 quarters + 9 nickels

14.

1 quarter + 9 dimes	11 nickels + 64 pennies

15.

4 quarters + 10 dimes	10 dimes + 100 pennies

16.

\$6.35 + 3.49	\$9.67 - 7.38	\$8.24 + 1.75	\$9.95 - 5.62

1.	$7\overline{)56}$	$7\overline{)28}$	$7\overline{)14}$	$7\overline{)42}$	$7\overline{)63}$
2.	$7\overline{)49}$	$7\overline{)35}$	$7\overline{)21}$	$7\overline{)7}$	$7\overline{)84}$
3.	$7\overline{)84}$	$7\overline{)77}$	$7\overline{)0}$	$7\overline{)70}$	$7\overline{)63}$
4.	$7\overline{)84}$	$7\overline{)7}$	$7\overline{)21}$	$7\overline{)35}$	$7\overline{)49}$
5.	$7\overline{)63}$	$7\overline{)42}$	$7\overline{)14}$	$7\overline{)28}$	$7\overline{)56}$
6.	504 - 468	807 - 549	605 - 389	903 - 818	302 - 258
7.	501 - 467	702 - 627	802 - 596	906 - 658	703 - 677
8.	804 - 537	904 - 829	908 - 569	402 - 337	906 - 649

"Praise him for his mighty acts." Psalm 150:2

9. 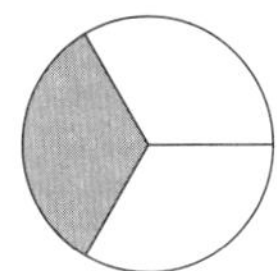 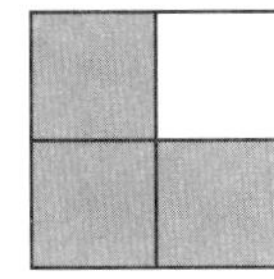 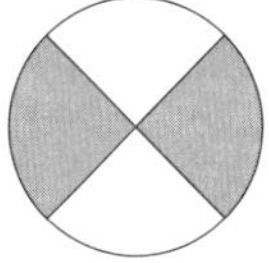 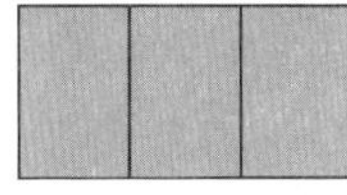

10. 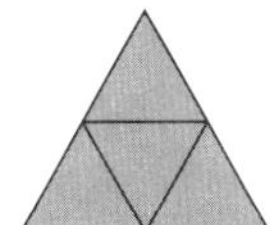 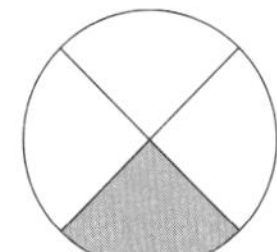 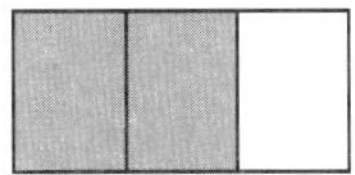 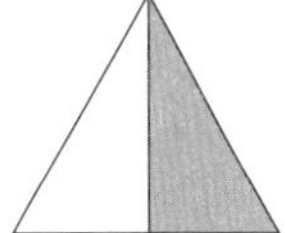

11. Fay's family made cookies for older people. They filled each bag with 12 cookies. There were 7 bags. How many cookies was that in all?

12. God made the sea horse on the fifth day. He made one kind that is 12 inches long. He made another kind 4 inches long. What is the difference in the number of inches?

13. 154 shrimp swam in a glass tank. A sea horse sucked in 38 of them. How many shrimp were left?

1.	$7\overline{)42}$	$7\overline{)56}$	$7\overline{)84}$	$7\overline{)70}$	$7\overline{)28}$
2.	$7\overline{)35}$	$7\overline{)84}$	$7\overline{)14}$	$7\overline{)77}$	$7\overline{)7}$
3.	$7\overline{)49}$	$7\overline{)63}$	$7\overline{)21}$	$7\overline{)0}$	$7\overline{)63}$
4.	$7\overline{)63}$	$7\overline{)0}$	$7\overline{)21}$	$7\overline{)63}$	$7\overline{)49}$
5.	$7\overline{)7}$	$7\overline{)77}$	$7\overline{)14}$	$7\overline{)84}$	$7\overline{)35}$
6.	$7\overline{)28}$	$7\overline{)70}$	$7\overline{)84}$	$7\overline{)56}$	$7\overline{)42}$
7.	$\begin{array}{r}807\\-389\\\hline\end{array}$	$\begin{array}{r}905\\-276\\\hline\end{array}$	$\begin{array}{r}703\\-467\\\hline\end{array}$	$\begin{array}{r}906\\-859\\\hline\end{array}$	$\begin{array}{r}602\\-537\\\hline\end{array}$
8.	$\begin{array}{r}804\\-185\\\hline\end{array}$	$\begin{array}{r}906\\-498\\\hline\end{array}$	$\begin{array}{r}505\\-468\\\hline\end{array}$	$\begin{array}{r}804\\-578\\\hline\end{array}$	$\begin{array}{r}303\\-248\\\hline\end{array}$

"Praise him for his mighty acts." Psalm 150:2

9. 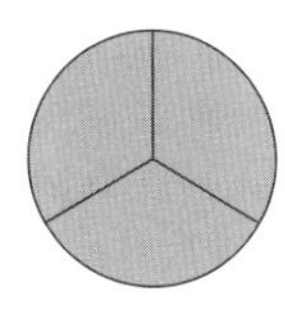 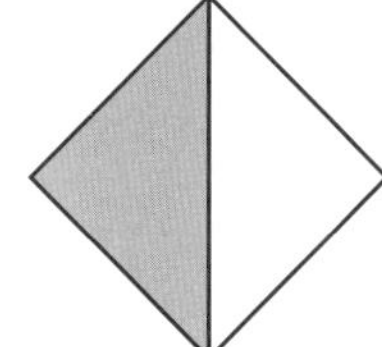 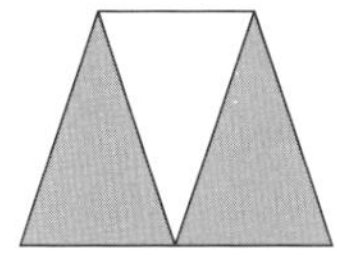 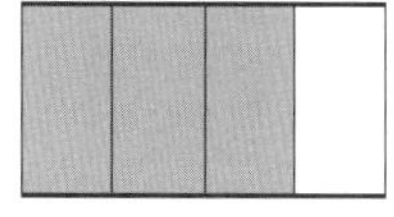

10. 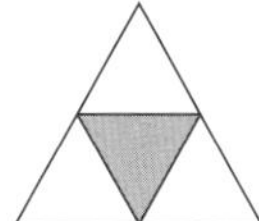 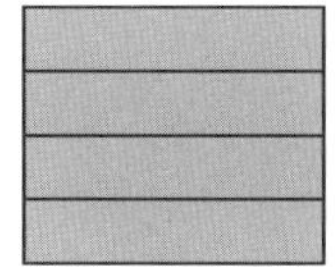 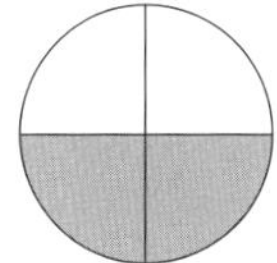 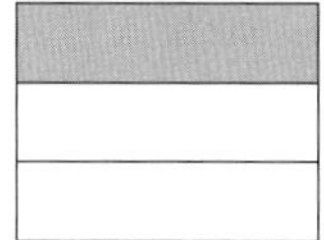

11. $6 \times 7 + 3 =$ $2 \times 12 + 3 =$

12. $6 \times 6 + 3 =$ $3 \times 7 + 3 =$

13. $6 \times 10 + 3 =$ $5 \times 12 + 3 =$

14. $7 \times 3 + 3 =$ $4 \times 9 + 3 =$

15. $6 \times 4 + 3 =$ $7 \times 6 + 3 =$

16. Mother's stove is 36 inches wide. How many yards is that? *Write the rule.*

17. Henry's bed is 1 yard wide. How many inches is that? *Write the rule.*

1.	$7\overline{)63}$	$7\overline{)49}$	$7\overline{)35}$	$7\overline{)21}$	$6\overline{)72}$
2.	$7\overline{)56}$	$7\overline{)14}$	$6\overline{)66}$	$7\overline{)56}$	$6\overline{)54}$
3.	$7\overline{)84}$	$6\overline{)18}$	$7\overline{)28}$	$6\overline{)42}$	$6\overline{)54}$
4.	$7\overline{)63}$	$6\overline{)48}$	$7\overline{)77}$	$6\overline{)12}$	$6\overline{)48}$
5.	$7\overline{)42}$	$7\overline{)70}$	$7\overline{)49}$	$6\overline{)60}$	$6\overline{)36}$

6.	$4\overline{)84}$	$4\overline{)80}$	$2\overline{)82}$	$2\overline{)40}$	$3\overline{)63}$
7.	$3\overline{)63}$	$3\overline{)60}$	$2\overline{)84}$	$2\overline{)40}$	$2\overline{)42}$
8.	$4\overline{)88}$	$4\overline{)48}$	$3\overline{)33}$	$2\overline{)20}$	$3\overline{)69}$
9.	$2\overline{)46}$	$4\overline{)40}$	$4\overline{)44}$	$2\overline{)24}$	$3\overline{)66}$

"Praise him for his mighty acts." Psalm 150:2

Write the Roman numerals.

10. 6 9 8 10

11. 8 7 10 9

12.

$$\begin{array}{r} 2 \text{ quarters} \\ + 50 \text{ pennies} \\ \hline \end{array} \qquad \begin{array}{r} 1 \text{ quarter} \\ + 9 \text{ dimes} \\ \hline \end{array}$$

13.

$$\begin{array}{r} 4 \text{ quarters} \\ + 5 \text{ nickels} \\ \hline \end{array} \qquad \begin{array}{r} 11 \text{ nickels} \\ + 94 \text{ pennies} \\ \hline \end{array}$$

14.

$$\begin{array}{r} 10 \text{ dimes} \\ + 7 \text{ nickels} \\ \hline \end{array} \qquad \begin{array}{r} 4 \text{ quarters} \\ + 6 \text{ dimes} \\ \hline \end{array}$$

15.

$$\begin{array}{r} 3 \text{ quarters} \\ + 12 \text{ nickels} \\ \hline \end{array} \qquad \begin{array}{r} 8 \text{ dimes} \\ + 96 \text{ pennies} \\ \hline \end{array}$$

16. Father made a chest for Mother that was 1 yard long. How many inches was that? *Write the rule.*

1.	$6\overline{)54}$	$6\overline{)42}$	$6\overline{)48}$	$7\overline{)56}$	$6\overline{)72}$
2.	$6\overline{)60}$	$7\overline{)63}$	$5\overline{)25}$	$5\overline{)30}$	$7\overline{)28}$
3.	$6\overline{)36}$	$7\overline{)14}$	$7\overline{)0}$	$6\overline{)12}$	$5\overline{)30}$
4.	$5\overline{)50}$	$7\overline{)42}$	$7\overline{)35}$	$6\overline{)54}$	$6\overline{)24}$
5.	$5\overline{)45}$	$7\overline{)56}$	$5\overline{)40}$	$7\overline{)49}$	$5\overline{)60}$

6.	$4\overline{)48}$	$4\overline{)80}$	$3\overline{)33}$	$4\overline{)84}$	$3\overline{)30}$
7.	$3\overline{)96}$	$3\overline{)69}$	$3\overline{)90}$	$4\overline{)40}$	$3\overline{)63}$
8.	$2\overline{)60}$	$2\overline{)46}$	$2\overline{)64}$	$4\overline{)88}$	$3\overline{)93}$
9.	$4\overline{)44}$	$2\overline{)40}$	$3\overline{)36}$	$2\overline{)62}$	$2\overline{)44}$

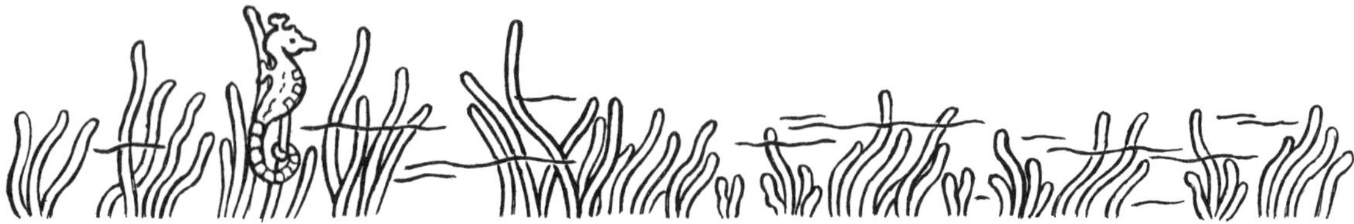

"Praise him for his mighty acts." Psalm 150:2

10. 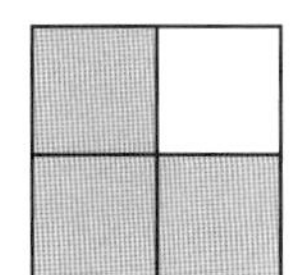 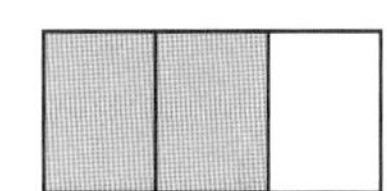 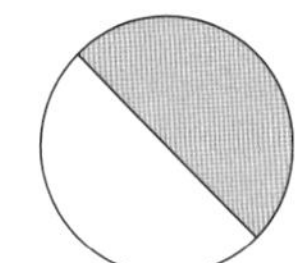 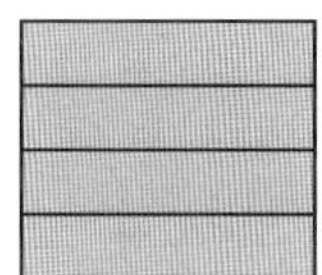

11. 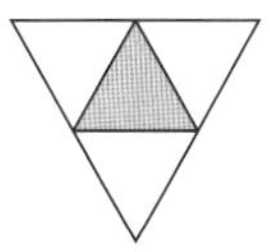 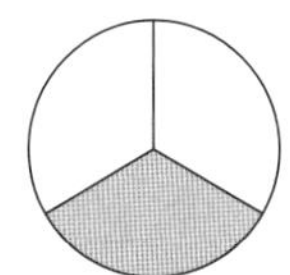 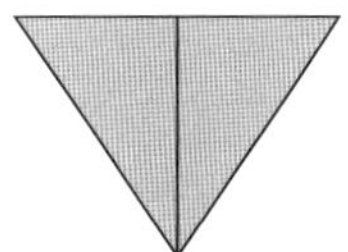 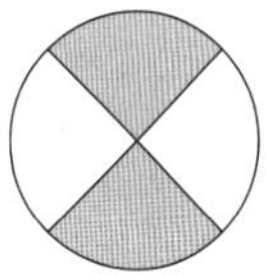

12. $\frac{1}{3}$ of 30 $\frac{1}{3}$ of 33 $\frac{1}{3}$ of 18

13. $\frac{1}{3}$ of 27 $\frac{1}{3}$ of 15 $\frac{1}{3}$ of 24

14. $\frac{1}{3}$ of 12 $\frac{1}{3}$ of 36 $\frac{1}{3}$ of 21

15. $\begin{array}{r} \$7.86 \\ -\ .48 \\ \hline \end{array}$ $\begin{array}{r} \$2.74 \\ +\ 5.96 \\ \hline \end{array}$ $\begin{array}{r} \$8.90 \\ -\ 6.39 \\ \hline \end{array}$ $\begin{array}{r} \$6.63 \\ +\ .97 \\ \hline \end{array}$

16. $\begin{array}{r} \$9.80 \\ -\ 5.38 \\ \hline \end{array}$ $\begin{array}{r} \$\ .68 \\ +\ .89 \\ \hline \end{array}$ $\begin{array}{r} \$4.39 \\ +\ 2.99 \\ \hline \end{array}$ $\begin{array}{r} \$9.57 \\ -\ .87 \\ \hline \end{array}$

17. $\begin{array}{r} \$1.64 \\ +\ .87 \\ \hline \end{array}$ $\begin{array}{r} \$9.50 \\ -\ 1.90 \\ \hline \end{array}$ $\begin{array}{r} \$4.22 \\ -\ .80 \\ \hline \end{array}$ $\begin{array}{r} \$\ .82 \\ -\ .25 \\ \hline \end{array}$

1.	$7\overline{)84}$	$5\overline{)45}$	$7\overline{)21}$	$6\overline{)12}$	$7\overline{)49}$
2.	$6\overline{)18}$	$7\overline{)14}$	$6\overline{)60}$	$5\overline{)40}$	$6\overline{)42}$
3.	$7\overline{)70}$	$4\overline{)32}$	$5\overline{)30}$	$7\overline{)35}$	$5\overline{)50}$
4.	$4\overline{)24}$	$6\overline{)30}$	$5\overline{)60}$	$4\overline{)28}$	$7\overline{)42}$
5.	$4\overline{)48}$	$5\overline{)35}$	$6\overline{)54}$	$5\overline{)25}$	$4\overline{)40}$
6.	$7\overline{)63}$	$4\overline{)20}$	$5\overline{)20}$	$7\overline{)28}$	$6\overline{)36}$
7.	$4\overline{)16}$	$6\overline{)24}$	$5\overline{)15}$	$4\overline{)8}$	$7\overline{)77}$
8.	$4\overline{)12}$	$5\overline{)10}$	$7\overline{)56}$	$6\overline{)6}$	$7\overline{)42}$
9.	$6\overline{)48}$	$7\overline{)7}$	$6\overline{)72}$	$4\overline{)36}$	$6\overline{)66}$

"Praise him for his mighty acts." Psalm 150:2

10. $4 \times 9 + 2 =$ $4 \times 6 + 3 =$

11. $3 \times 8 + 3 =$ $3 \times 12 + 2 =$

12. $3 \times 7 + 2 =$ $4 \times 4 + 3 =$

13. $3 \times 6 + 1 =$ $4 \times 5 + 3 =$

14. At church 9 people sat on each bench. How many people sat on six benches?

15. Mother read *Little Pilgrim's Progress* to the family. She read 4 chapters each evening. How many chapters did she read in five evenings?

16. God made many kinds of sea horses. Fay saw pictures of 24 kinds. Rose saw pictures of 19 kinds. How many more kinds did Fay see than Rose?

1.	7)49	7)35	7)63	5)30	6)72
2.	6)54	4)24	5)45	3)36	7)42
3.	4)36	2)24	3)21	1)9	7)21
4.	2)14	7)63	7)28	3)27	5)35
5.	6)24	2)18	5)40	3)18	7)0
6.	4)32	2)12	5)25	3)9	4)28
7.	4)20	4)12	2)16	6)66	6)18
8.	3)24	7)77	7)56	4)40	6)36
9.	6)48	7)70	6)42	6)30	7)84

"Praise him for his mighty acts." Psalm 150:2

Write the Roman numerals.

10. 3 5 6 8

11. 10 4 7 9

12.

13.

14. From the Bible we know that Jesus' parents went to Jerusalem every 365 days. How many years was that? *Write the rule.*

15. Father gave 16 ounces of mints to Mother for her birthday. How many pounds was that? *Write the rule.*

16. Milton painted a gate that was 36 inches wide. How many yards was that? *Write the rule.*

1.	7)63	7)49	7)35	6)24	5)45
2.	5)60	4)36	7)28	6)30	6)42
3.	4)28	3)24	4)24	3)15	7)70
4.	3)33	6)60	4)20	3)18	4)32
5.	7)56	7)84	7)77	6)66	6)72
6.	4)44	7)56	1)9	3)9	7)14
7.	3)21	6)12	1)3	2)18	6)48
8.	4)48	7)42	7)70	5)35	7)21
9.	6)54	6)18	6)42	6)60	6)36

"Praise him for his mighty acts." Psalm 150:2

10. $6 \times 6 =$ $7 \times 9 =$ $7 \times 8 =$

11. $7 \times 5 =$ $5 \times 11 =$ $5 \times 10 =$

12. $6 \times 9 =$ $7 \times 7 =$ $7 \times 10 =$

13. $6 \times 8 =$ $6 \times 10 =$ $5 \times 12 =$

14.

48	54	65	32	83	32
49	55	4	44	73	56
+ 50	+ 56	+ 98	+ 78	+ 7	+ 59

15.

67	61	43	54	73	84
12	23	40	34	4	5
+ 89	+ 79	+ 61	+ 79	+ 88	+ 79

16. In *Life Songs* there are 343 songs. A blind lady wrote 24 of the songs. How many songs were written by other people?

17. Mother put $\frac{1}{2}$ dozen mints at each person's plate. There were seven plates. How many mints was that altogether?

121

1.	0 × 8	1 × 8	2 × 8	3 × 8	4 × 8	5 × 8	6 × 8
2.	7 × 8	8 × 8	9 × 8	10 × 8	11 × 8	12 × 8	
3.	8 × 8	6 × 8	12 × 8	4 × 8	10 × 8	7 × 8	9 × 8
4.	7 × 8	10 × 8	4 × 8	2 × 8	11 × 8	3 × 8	5 × 8
5.	3 × 8	11 × 8	2 × 8	6 × 8	9 × 8	1 × 8	0 × 8
6.	1 × 8	9 × 8	6 × 8	7 × 8	12 × 8	8 × 8	5 × 8
7.	8 × 8	12 × 8	7 × 8	12 × 8	6 × 8	8 × 8	9 × 8

Write the Roman numerals.

8. 10 4 8 6

9. 3 9 5 7

10. $4 \times 12 + 2 =$ $5 \times 9 + 2 =$

11. $7 \times 8 + 1 =$ $4 \times 8 + 3 =$

12. $6 \times 9 + 3 =$ $3 \times 11 + 2 =$

13. $6 \times 8 + 2 =$ $4 \times 11 + 3 =$

14. $7 \times 9 + 1 =$

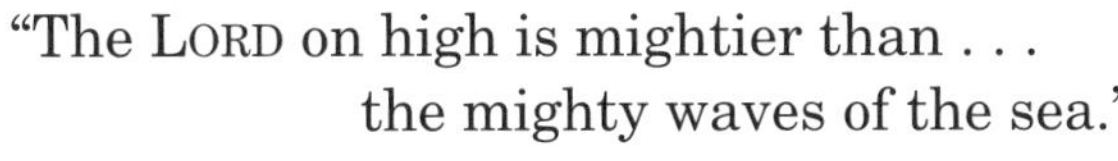

"The LORD on high is mightier than . . .
the mighty waves of the sea."

Psalm 93:4

1. 9×8 $\quad 12 \times 8$ $\quad 10 \times 8$ $\quad 7 \times 8$ $\quad 5 \times 8$ $\quad 3 \times 8$ $\quad 11 \times 8$

2. 3×8 $\quad 5 \times 8$ $\quad 7 \times 8$ $\quad 2 \times 8$ $\quad 4 \times 8$ $\quad 6 \times 8$ $\quad 8 \times 8$

3. 6×8 $\quad 4 \times 8$ $\quad 2 \times 8$ $\quad 9 \times 8$ $\quad 1 \times 8$ $\quad 0 \times 8$ $\quad 8 \times 8$

4. 0×8 $\quad 1 \times 8$ $\quad 9 \times 8$ $\quad 10 \times 8$ $\quad 12 \times 8$ $\quad 9 \times 8$ $\quad 11 \times 8$

5. 70×8 $\quad 60 \times 6$ $\quad 91 \times 7$ $\quad 71 \times 7$ $\quad 64 \times 2$ $\quad 60 \times 8$

6. 61×6 $\quad 90 \times 7$ $\quad 31 \times 8$ $\quad 41 \times 8$ $\quad 43 \times 3$ $\quad 81 \times 8$

7. 81×4 $\quad 20 \times 8$ $\quad 90 \times 4$ $\quad 80 \times 7$ $\quad 32 \times 4$ $\quad 80 \times 6$

"The voice of the LORD is upon the waters." Psalm 29:3

8.

2 half dollars	2 half dollars
+ 3 quarters	+ 4 quarters

9.

2 half dollars	1 half dollar
+ 13 nickels	+ 2 quarters

10.

1 half dollar	1 half dollar
+ 83 pennies	+ 9 dimes

11.

$ .89	$1.77	$3.66	$2.48
+ .43	− .39	+ .89	+ 3.89

12.

$8.63	$9.90	$1.64	$ .64
− 2.27	− 5.36	− .27	+ .67

13. Norma stayed with Grandmother for 7 days to help her. How many weeks was that? *Write the rule.*

14. When Gordon broke his leg, he was in the hospital for 1 week. How many days was that? *Write the rule.*

1. 7×8 10×8 6×8 4×8 2×8 0×8 8×8

2. 9×8 11×8 5×8 3×8 1×8 9×8 7×8

3. 7×8 9×8 1×8 3×8 5×8 11×8 9×8

4. 8×8 0×8 2×8 4×8 6×8 10×8 7×8

5. 82×2 31×8 64×2 62×3 50×3 81×6

6. 31×6 32×4 21×8 70×8 94×2 90×8

7. 84×2 80×7 62×4 41×4 30×5 61×8

"The voice of the LORD is upon the waters." Psalm 29:3

8. 2 half dollars
+ 2 quarters

1 half dollar
+ 7 dimes

9. 3 quarters
+ 12 nickels

2 half dollars
+ 1 quarter

10. 2 half dollars
+ 10 dimes

1 half dollar
+ 10 nickels

11. 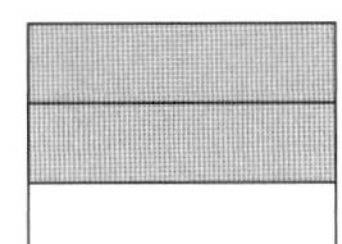 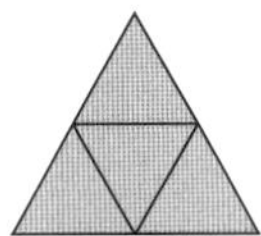 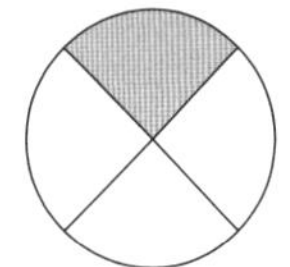

12. 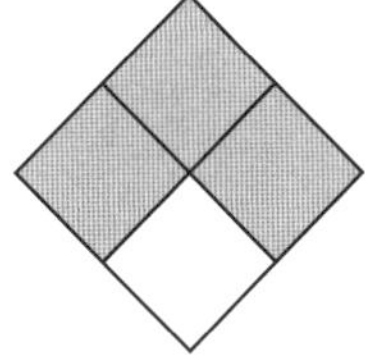 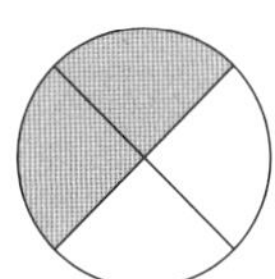 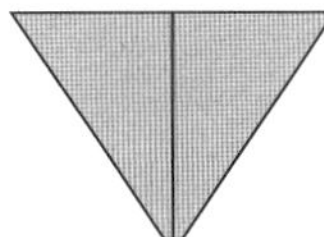 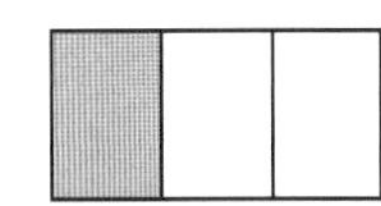

13. six thousand, seventy

14. four thousand, seven hundred eighty

15. five thousand, sixty-four

16. six thousand, nine hundred ninety

17. three thousand, fifty-two

124

1.	6 × 8	10 × 8	9 × 7	5 × 8	7 × 8	9 × 8	8 × 8
2.	7 × 7	4 × 8	3 × 7	4 × 7	6 × 7	12 × 8	12 × 7
3.	8 × 8	9 × 8	8 × 7	5 × 8	9 × 7	10 × 8	6 × 8
4.	12 × 7	12 × 8	6 × 7	4 × 7	3 × 7	4 × 8	7 × 7

5.	33 × 5	24 × 6	48 × 4	23 × 4	46 × 4	86 × 4
6.	46 × 2	24 × 8	36 × 2	39 × 2	15 × 4	14 × 5
7.	26 × 3	24 × 3	48 × 3	55 × 3	23 × 8	43 × 8

"The voice of the LORD is upon the waters." Psalm 29:3

1.
$$\begin{array}{r} 6 \\ \times 8 \\ \hline \end{array} \quad \begin{array}{r} 10 \\ \times 8 \\ \hline \end{array} \quad \begin{array}{r} 9 \\ \times 7 \\ \hline \end{array} \quad \begin{array}{r} 5 \\ \times 8 \\ \hline \end{array} \quad \begin{array}{r} 7 \\ \times 8 \\ \hline \end{array} \quad \begin{array}{r} 9 \\ \times 8 \\ \hline \end{array} \quad \begin{array}{r} 8 \\ \times 8 \\ \hline \end{array}$$

2.
$$\begin{array}{r} 7 \\ \times 7 \\ \hline \end{array} \quad \begin{array}{r} 4 \\ \times 8 \\ \hline \end{array} \quad \begin{array}{r} 3 \\ \times 7 \\ \hline \end{array} \quad \begin{array}{r} 4 \\ \times 7 \\ \hline \end{array} \quad \begin{array}{r} 6 \\ \times 7 \\ \hline \end{array} \quad \begin{array}{r} 12 \\ \times 8 \\ \hline \end{array} \quad \begin{array}{r} 12 \\ \times 7 \\ \hline \end{array}$$

3.
$$\begin{array}{r} 8 \\ \times 8 \\ \hline \end{array} \quad \begin{array}{r} 9 \\ \times 8 \\ \hline \end{array} \quad \begin{array}{r} 8 \\ \times 7 \\ \hline \end{array} \quad \begin{array}{r} 5 \\ \times 8 \\ \hline \end{array} \quad \begin{array}{r} 9 \\ \times 7 \\ \hline \end{array} \quad \begin{array}{r} 10 \\ \times 8 \\ \hline \end{array} \quad \begin{array}{r} 6 \\ \times 8 \\ \hline \end{array}$$

4.
$$\begin{array}{r} 12 \\ \times 7 \\ \hline \end{array} \quad \begin{array}{r} 12 \\ \times 8 \\ \hline \end{array} \quad \begin{array}{r} 6 \\ \times 7 \\ \hline \end{array} \quad \begin{array}{r} 4 \\ \times 7 \\ \hline \end{array} \quad \begin{array}{r} 3 \\ \times 7 \\ \hline \end{array} \quad \begin{array}{r} 4 \\ \times 8 \\ \hline \end{array} \quad \begin{array}{r} 7 \\ \times 7 \\ \hline \end{array}$$

~~~~~~

5.
$$\begin{array}{r} 33 \\ \times 5 \\ \hline \end{array} \quad \begin{array}{r} 24 \\ \times 6 \\ \hline \end{array} \quad \begin{array}{r} 48 \\ \times 4 \\ \hline \end{array} \quad \begin{array}{r} 23 \\ \times 4 \\ \hline \end{array} \quad \begin{array}{r} 46 \\ \times 4 \\ \hline \end{array} \quad \begin{array}{r} 86 \\ \times 4 \\ \hline \end{array}$$

6.
$$\begin{array}{r} 46 \\ \times 2 \\ \hline \end{array} \quad \begin{array}{r} 24 \\ \times 8 \\ \hline \end{array} \quad \begin{array}{r} 36 \\ \times 2 \\ \hline \end{array} \quad \begin{array}{r} 39 \\ \times 2 \\ \hline \end{array} \quad \begin{array}{r} 15 \\ \times 4 \\ \hline \end{array} \quad \begin{array}{r} 14 \\ \times 5 \\ \hline \end{array}$$

7.
$$\begin{array}{r} 26 \\ \times 3 \\ \hline \end{array} \quad \begin{array}{r} 24 \\ \times 3 \\ \hline \end{array} \quad \begin{array}{r} 48 \\ \times 3 \\ \hline \end{array} \quad \begin{array}{r} 55 \\ \times 3 \\ \hline \end{array} \quad \begin{array}{r} 23 \\ \times 8 \\ \hline \end{array} \quad \begin{array}{r} 43 \\ \times 8 \\ \hline \end{array}$$

"The voice of the LORD is upon the waters." Psalm 29:3

8.  

9.   

10. $16 - 9 + 3 =$ $\qquad$ $7 + 8 - 9 =$

11. $9 + 8 - 9 =$ $\qquad$ $12 - 4 + 8 =$

12. $13 - 4 + 7 =$ $\qquad$ $6 + 9 - 7 =$

13. $7 + 5 - 3 =$ $\qquad$ $14 - 8 + 4 =$

14. $15 - 6 + 8 =$ $\qquad$ $17 - 8 + 9 =$

15. $14 - 7 + 6 =$ $\qquad$ $17 - 9 + 5 =$

16. There are 9 flowers on each of Mother's plants. She has 7 plants. How many flowers is that?

1. 9×8 12×7 9×7 8×6 7×7 8×8 12×6

2. 12×8 8×7 6×8 7×6 6×7 7×8 9×6

3. 8×8 7×7 8×6 9×7 12×7 9×8 4×6

4. 7×8 6×7 7×6 6×8 8×7 12×8 9×8

5. 48×2 24×8 13×8 24×3 39×2 55×2

6. 36×2 26×4 63×8 14×6 16×5 15×6

7. 28×3 84×6 48×4 24×4 22×5 26×3

"The voice of the LORD is upon the waters." Psalm 29:3

125

1.
$$\begin{array}{r}9\\ \times\ 8\\ \hline\end{array}\qquad\begin{array}{r}12\\ \times\ 7\\ \hline\end{array}\qquad\begin{array}{r}9\\ \times\ 7\\ \hline\end{array}\qquad\begin{array}{r}8\\ \times\ 6\\ \hline\end{array}\qquad\begin{array}{r}7\\ \times\ 7\\ \hline\end{array}\qquad\begin{array}{r}8\\ \times\ 8\\ \hline\end{array}\qquad\begin{array}{r}12\\ \times\ 6\\ \hline\end{array}$$

2.
$$\begin{array}{r}12\\ \times\ 8\\ \hline\end{array}\qquad\begin{array}{r}8\\ \times\ 7\\ \hline\end{array}\qquad\begin{array}{r}6\\ \times\ 8\\ \hline\end{array}\qquad\begin{array}{r}7\\ \times\ 6\\ \hline\end{array}\qquad\begin{array}{r}6\\ \times\ 7\\ \hline\end{array}\qquad\begin{array}{r}7\\ \times\ 8\\ \hline\end{array}\qquad\begin{array}{r}9\\ \times\ 6\\ \hline\end{array}$$

3.
$$\begin{array}{r}8\\ \times\ 8\\ \hline\end{array}\qquad\begin{array}{r}7\\ \times\ 7\\ \hline\end{array}\qquad\begin{array}{r}8\\ \times\ 6\\ \hline\end{array}\qquad\begin{array}{r}9\\ \times\ 7\\ \hline\end{array}\qquad\begin{array}{r}12\\ \times\ 7\\ \hline\end{array}\qquad\begin{array}{r}9\\ \times\ 8\\ \hline\end{array}\qquad\begin{array}{r}4\\ \times\ 6\\ \hline\end{array}$$

4.
$$\begin{array}{r}7\\ \times\ 8\\ \hline\end{array}\qquad\begin{array}{r}6\\ \times\ 7\\ \hline\end{array}\qquad\begin{array}{r}7\\ \times\ 6\\ \hline\end{array}\qquad\begin{array}{r}6\\ \times\ 8\\ \hline\end{array}\qquad\begin{array}{r}8\\ \times\ 7\\ \hline\end{array}\qquad\begin{array}{r}12\\ \times\ 8\\ \hline\end{array}\qquad\begin{array}{r}9\\ \times\ 8\\ \hline\end{array}$$

5.
$$\begin{array}{r}48\\ \times\ 2\\ \hline\end{array}\qquad\begin{array}{r}24\\ \times\ 8\\ \hline\end{array}\qquad\begin{array}{r}13\\ \times\ 8\\ \hline\end{array}\qquad\begin{array}{r}24\\ \times\ 3\\ \hline\end{array}\qquad\begin{array}{r}39\\ \times\ 2\\ \hline\end{array}\qquad\begin{array}{r}55\\ \times\ 2\\ \hline\end{array}$$

6.
$$\begin{array}{r}36\\ \times\ 2\\ \hline\end{array}\qquad\begin{array}{r}26\\ \times\ 4\\ \hline\end{array}\qquad\begin{array}{r}63\\ \times\ 8\\ \hline\end{array}\qquad\begin{array}{r}14\\ \times\ 6\\ \hline\end{array}\qquad\begin{array}{r}16\\ \times\ 5\\ \hline\end{array}\qquad\begin{array}{r}15\\ \times\ 6\\ \hline\end{array}$$

7.
$$\begin{array}{r}28\\ \times\ 3\\ \hline\end{array}\qquad\begin{array}{r}84\\ \times\ 6\\ \hline\end{array}\qquad\begin{array}{r}48\\ \times\ 4\\ \hline\end{array}\qquad\begin{array}{r}24\\ \times\ 4\\ \hline\end{array}\qquad\begin{array}{r}22\\ \times\ 5\\ \hline\end{array}\qquad\begin{array}{r}26\\ \times\ 3\\ \hline\end{array}$$

"The voice of the LORD is upon the waters." Psalm 29:3

Write the Roman numerals.

8. 14 15 12 13

9. 15 13 14 11

10. Lee sold a hen for $6.94. He gave $1.25 of the money to the Lord's work. He bought a notebook with the rest. How much did he pay for the notebook?

11. Jane helped to make beds. She spread three blankets on each bed. There were 6 beds. How many blankets was that in all?

12. God made fishes and frogs for the otter to eat. A large otter eats 3 pounds of food each day. How many pounds does he eat in 8 days?

1. 6×8 8×5 12×8 7×7 9×6 5×6 6×6

2. 5×8 8×6 7×7 12×8 6×5 9×6 5×7

3. 5×5 9×8 12×7 8×7 7×6 8×8 9×7

4. 4×6 12×7 9×8 6×7 7×8 9×7 8×8

5. 34×8 13×6 46×4 93×4 47×3 54×8

6. 62×6 23×8 34×6 36×4 83×5 52×8

7. 24×6 68×3 26×3 68×4 86×5 35×4

"The voice of the LORD is upon the waters." Psalm 29:3

Write the Roman numerals.

8. 12 14 13 15

9. 11 13 15 14

10. $\frac{1}{4}$ of 48 $\frac{1}{4}$ of 16 $\frac{1}{3}$ of 33

11. $\frac{1}{2}$ of 20 $\frac{1}{3}$ of 9 $\frac{1}{4}$ of 36

12. $\frac{1}{4}$ of 32 $\frac{1}{4}$ of 8 $\frac{1}{4}$ of 28

13. $\frac{1}{3}$ of 18 $\frac{1}{2}$ of 24 $\frac{1}{3}$ of 15

14. The Bible says that Noah and his family were in the ark 7 days before God sent the Flood. How many weeks was that? *Write the rule.*

15. Keith made a tail for his kite that was 1 yard long. How many inches was that? *Write the rule.*

1.	5 × 8	8 × 6	12 × 3	9 × 3	9 × 4	6 × 8	8 × 5
2.	7 × 6	8 × 7	4 × 8	6 × 4	2 × 8	9 × 7	9 × 5
3.	7 × 8	6 × 7	8 × 3	8 × 4	9 × 7	2 × 8	11 × 4
4.	6 × 5	8 × 8	7 × 3	12 × 2	3 × 7	8 × 8	5 × 6
5.	9 × 8	12 × 5	7 × 4	6 × 3	9 × 6	8 × 2	10 × 5
6.	10 × 6	9 × 8	3 × 6	4 × 7	4 × 4	9 × 6	7 × 7
7.	4 × 5	12 × 8	3 × 4	6 × 6	12 × 1	12 × 8	5 × 4

"The voice of the LORD is upon the waters." Psalm 29:3

8. 

9.   

10.	$\frac{1}{2}$ of 6	$\frac{1}{3}$ of 36	$\frac{1}{3}$ of 12
11.	$\frac{1}{4}$ of 20	$\frac{1}{4}$ of 44	$\frac{1}{3}$ of 18
12.	$\frac{1}{3}$ of 21	$\frac{1}{4}$ of 48	$\frac{1}{4}$ of 32
13.	$\frac{1}{2}$ of 18	$\frac{1}{2}$ of 22	$\frac{1}{2}$ of 20

14. The Bible tells about a breastplate that had pretty stones on it. 3 stones were in each row. There were 4 rows. How many stones was that altogether?

1. $\begin{array}{r}6\\\times 8\\\hline\end{array}$ $\begin{array}{r}9\\\times 8\\\hline\end{array}$ $\begin{array}{r}9\\\times 4\\\hline\end{array}$ $\begin{array}{r}6\\\times 7\\\hline\end{array}$ $\begin{array}{r}12\\\times 8\\\hline\end{array}$ $\begin{array}{r}7\\\times 3\\\hline\end{array}$ $\begin{array}{r}11\\\times 5\\\hline\end{array}$

2. $\begin{array}{r}7\\\times 7\\\hline\end{array}$ $\begin{array}{r}3\\\times 7\\\hline\end{array}$ $\begin{array}{r}12\\\times 8\\\hline\end{array}$ $\begin{array}{r}7\\\times 6\\\hline\end{array}$ $\begin{array}{r}6\\\times 6\\\hline\end{array}$ $\begin{array}{r}9\\\times 8\\\hline\end{array}$ $\begin{array}{r}9\\\times 6\\\hline\end{array}$

3. $\begin{array}{r}7\\\times 8\\\hline\end{array}$ $\begin{array}{r}4\\\times 8\\\hline\end{array}$ $\begin{array}{r}2\\\times 8\\\hline\end{array}$ $\begin{array}{r}3\\\times 2\\\hline\end{array}$ $\begin{array}{r}7\\\times 4\\\hline\end{array}$ $\begin{array}{r}0\\\times 8\\\hline\end{array}$ $\begin{array}{r}8\\\times 8\\\hline\end{array}$

4. $\begin{array}{r}8\\\times 4\\\hline\end{array}$ $\begin{array}{r}8\\\times 7\\\hline\end{array}$ $\begin{array}{r}2\\\times 3\\\hline\end{array}$ $\begin{array}{r}8\\\times 2\\\hline\end{array}$ $\begin{array}{r}0\\\times 1\\\hline\end{array}$ $\begin{array}{r}4\\\times 7\\\hline\end{array}$ $\begin{array}{r}9\\\times 7\\\hline\end{array}$

5. $5\overline{)45}$ $7\overline{)42}$ $5\overline{)25}$ $7\overline{)42}$ $7\overline{)63}$

6. $7\overline{)56}$ $7\overline{)28}$ $6\overline{)72}$ $6\overline{)36}$ $6\overline{)30}$

7. $5\overline{)20}$ $6\overline{)48}$ $5\overline{)30}$ $7\overline{)84}$ $7\overline{)35}$

8. $6\overline{)42}$ $6\overline{)24}$ $4\overline{)16}$ $5\overline{)20}$ $7\overline{)49}$

"The voice of the LORD is upon the waters." Psalm 29:3

Write the Roman numerals.

9. 12 13 14 15

10. 11 14 13 15

11.

$$\begin{array}{r l} 2 & \text{half dollars} \\ +\ 4 & \text{quarters} \\ \hline \end{array} \qquad \begin{array}{r l} 2 & \text{quarters} \\ +\ 12 & \text{nickels} \\ \hline \end{array}$$

12.

$$\begin{array}{r l} 1 & \text{half dollar} \\ +\ 10 & \text{nickels} \\ \hline \end{array} \qquad \begin{array}{r l} 1 & \text{half dollar} \\ +\ 3 & \text{quarters} \\ \hline \end{array}$$

13.

$$\begin{array}{r l} 10 & \text{dimes} \\ +\ 3 & \text{quarters} \\ \hline \end{array} \qquad \begin{array}{r l} 2 & \text{half dollars} \\ +\ 8 & \text{dimes} \\ \hline \end{array}$$

14.

$$\begin{array}{r} 861 \\ -\ 502 \\ \hline \end{array} \quad \begin{array}{r} 606 \\ -\ 249 \\ \hline \end{array} \quad \begin{array}{r} 438 \\ +\ 977 \\ \hline \end{array} \quad \begin{array}{r} 543 \\ +\ 866 \\ \hline \end{array} \quad \begin{array}{r} 502 \\ -\ 65 \\ \hline \end{array}$$

15.

$$\begin{array}{r} 829 \\ -\ 392 \\ \hline \end{array} \quad \begin{array}{r} 632 \\ +\ 777 \\ \hline \end{array} \quad \begin{array}{r} 637 \\ +\ 878 \\ \hline \end{array} \quad \begin{array}{r} 393 \\ -\ 36 \\ \hline \end{array} \quad \begin{array}{r} 785 \\ -\ 426 \\ \hline \end{array}$$

129

1. $8\overline{)0}$ $8\overline{)8}$ $8\overline{)16}$ $8\overline{)24}$ $8\overline{)32}$

2. $8\overline{)40}$ $8\overline{)48}$ $8\overline{)56}$ $8\overline{)64}$ $8\overline{)72}$

3. $8\overline{)80}$ $8\overline{)88}$ $8\overline{)96}$

4. $8\overline{)72}$ $8\overline{)56}$ $8\overline{)24}$ $8\overline{)64}$ $8\overline{)32}$

5. $8\overline{)64}$ $8\overline{)24}$ $8\overline{)56}$ $8\overline{)72}$ $8\overline{)88}$

6. $8\overline{)48}$ $8\overline{)72}$ $8\overline{)96}$ $8\overline{)16}$ $8\overline{)8}$

7. $8\overline{)72}$ $8\overline{)48}$ $8\overline{)16}$ $8\overline{)96}$ $8\overline{)0}$

8. $8\overline{)40}$ $8\overline{)80}$ $8\overline{)64}$ $8\overline{)96}$ $8\overline{)88}$

9. $8\overline{)96}$ $8\overline{)64}$ $8\overline{)80}$ $8\overline{)40}$ $8\overline{)32}$

"All the rivers run into the sea." Ecclesiastes 1:7

10. $\frac{1}{4}$ of 8 $\frac{1}{3}$ of 12 $\frac{1}{2}$ of 12

11. $\frac{1}{2}$ of 20 $\frac{1}{4}$ of 36 $\frac{1}{3}$ of 24

12. $\frac{1}{4}$ of 12 $\frac{1}{4}$ of 20 $\frac{1}{2}$ of 14

13. $\frac{1}{3}$ of 33 $\frac{1}{4}$ of 48 $\frac{1}{2}$ of 24

14. $\begin{array}{r} 249 \\ +\ 659 \\ \hline \end{array}$ $\begin{array}{r} 649 \\ -\ 77 \\ \hline \end{array}$ $\begin{array}{r} 659 \\ -\ 386 \\ \hline \end{array}$ $\begin{array}{r} 783 \\ +\ 675 \\ \hline \end{array}$ $\begin{array}{r} 477 \\ +\ 46 \\ \hline \end{array}$

15. $\begin{array}{r} 869 \\ +\ 366 \\ \hline \end{array}$ $\begin{array}{r} 803 \\ -\ 476 \\ \hline \end{array}$ $\begin{array}{r} 865 \\ -\ 295 \\ \hline \end{array}$ $\begin{array}{r} 394 \\ -\ 66 \\ \hline \end{array}$ $\begin{array}{r} 466 \\ +\ 770 \\ \hline \end{array}$

16. $\begin{array}{r} 868 \\ -\ 297 \\ \hline \end{array}$ $\begin{array}{r} 539 \\ +\ 368 \\ \hline \end{array}$ $\begin{array}{r} 563 \\ +\ 894 \\ \hline \end{array}$ $\begin{array}{r} 301 \\ -\ 29 \\ \hline \end{array}$ $\begin{array}{r} 980 \\ -\ 458 \\ \hline \end{array}$

17. In 1 week Mother got her garden seeds in the mail. How many days was that? *Write the rule.*

1.	$8\overline{)96}$	$8\overline{)56}$	$8\overline{)24}$	$8\overline{)72}$	$8\overline{)32}$
2.	$8\overline{)64}$	$8\overline{)24}$	$8\overline{)56}$	$8\overline{)32}$	$8\overline{)72}$
3.	$8\overline{)0}$	$8\overline{)88}$	$8\overline{)48}$	$8\overline{)72}$	$8\overline{)56}$
4.	$8\overline{)8}$	$8\overline{)40}$	$8\overline{)80}$	$8\overline{)16}$	$8\overline{)72}$
5.	$8\overline{)64}$	$8\overline{)72}$	$8\overline{)16}$	$8\overline{)80}$	$8\overline{)40}$
6.	$8\overline{)96}$	$8\overline{)56}$	$8\overline{)72}$	$8\overline{)48}$	$8\overline{)88}$

7.	48×4	33×8	84×6	46×3	93×4	54×8
8.	62×6	23×6	63×8	66×4	24×8	86×5

"All the rivers run into the sea." Ecclesiastes 1:7

9. $7 \times 8 + 1 =$ $8 \times 8 + 2 =$

10. $7 \times 10 + 2 =$ $6 \times 12 + 1 =$

11. $6 \times 9 + 3 =$ $7 \times 9 + 3 =$

12. $6 \times 8 + 2 =$ $5 \times 11 + 3 =$

13. Carl sold a puppy for $9.73 and a rabbit for $5.59. How much more did he get for the puppy than for the rabbit?

14. An otter swam 7 miles each hour. How many miles did it swim in three hours?

15. Father watered $\frac{1}{2}$ dozen plants in each row. There were 8 rows. How many plants was that in all?

1.	$8\overline{)64}$	$8\overline{)56}$	$8\overline{)40}$	$8\overline{)16}$	$8\overline{)72}$
2.	$8\overline{)24}$	$8\overline{)80}$	$8\overline{)72}$	$8\overline{)32}$	$8\overline{)96}$
3.	$8\overline{)48}$	$8\overline{)8}$	$8\overline{)0}$	$8\overline{)48}$	$8\overline{)88}$
4.	$8\overline{)32}$	$8\overline{)72}$	$8\overline{)80}$	$8\overline{)24}$	$8\overline{)96}$
5.	$8\overline{)16}$	$8\overline{)40}$	$8\overline{)56}$	$8\overline{)64}$	$8\overline{)72}$

6.	47×3	80×7	68×2	82×3	69×4	82×2
7.	89×4	73×3	95×6	91×8	75×6	43×2
8.	35×4	34×4	70×8	46×6	41×6	41×4

"All the rivers run into the sea." Ecclesiastes 1:7

9.  

10.   

11.

22	83	34	45	37	46
67	4	45	22	40	53
+ 4	+ 92	+ 88	+ 86	+ 94	+ 6

12.

57	35	96	26	52	33
42	34	80	62	16	56
+ 5	+ 97	+ 2	+ 82	+ 84	+ 3

13. For 12 months Glen wrote in a notebook what kind of weather God sent each day. How many years was that? *Write the rule.*

14. After your birthday you need to wait 1 year to have another birthday. How many months is that? *Write the rule.*

1. $8\overline{)72}$ $8\overline{)96}$ $7\overline{)21}$ $7\overline{)28}$ $8\overline{)48}$

2. $7\overline{)84}$ $7\overline{)63}$ $8\overline{)32}$ $8\overline{)24}$ $8\overline{)16}$

3. $8\overline{)64}$ $8\overline{)88}$ $8\overline{)0}$ $7\overline{)77}$ $7\overline{)56}$

4. $8\overline{)56}$ $8\overline{)40}$ $8\overline{)80}$ $8\overline{)8}$ $7\overline{)14}$

5. $7\overline{)35}$ $7\overline{)49}$ $7\overline{)7}$ $7\overline{)70}$ $7\overline{)42}$

6. 80×7 82×8 63×8 42×4 72×7 82×8

7. 84×2 84×6 28×3 68×4 87×4 23×3

8. 21×4 34×8 70×8 28×2 73×6 83×8

"All the rivers run into the sea." Ecclesiastes 1:7

Write the Roman numerals.

9. 14 13 10 9

10. 15 12 11 8

11.

1 dollar + 1 half dollar	5 dollars + 4 quarters

12.

2 dollars + 7 dimes	6 dollars + 2 quarters

13.

3 dollars + 3 quarters	7 dollars + 2 half dollars

14.

4 dollars + 12 nickels	9 dollars + 11 nickels

15. Fern goes to the dentist every 12 months. How many years is that? *Write the rule.*

16. Henry helped to plant $\frac{1}{2}$ dozen rows of peas. How many rows was that? *Write the rule.*

1.	$8\overline{)56}$	$6\overline{)48}$	$8\overline{)32}$	$8\overline{)16}$	$8\overline{)72}$
2.	$6\overline{)54}$	$8\overline{)80}$	$6\overline{)72}$	$6\overline{)24}$	$8\overline{)24}$
3.	$6\overline{)18}$	$8\overline{)32}$	$8\overline{)96}$	$7\overline{)70}$	$8\overline{)72}$
4.	$7\overline{)63}$	$6\overline{)12}$	$7\overline{)28}$	$8\overline{)64}$	$7\overline{)49}$
5.	$8\overline{)64}$	$8\overline{)40}$	$8\overline{)0}$	$7\overline{)35}$	$7\overline{)56}$
6.	$6\overline{)42}$	$7\overline{)84}$	$7\overline{)28}$	$8\overline{)24}$	$8\overline{)88}$
7.	$8\overline{)96}$	$8\overline{)56}$	$7\overline{)21}$	$8\overline{)32}$	$7\overline{)77}$
8.	$8\overline{)48}$	$6\overline{)36}$	$8\overline{)8}$	$8\overline{)48}$	$7\overline{)42}$
9.	$7\overline{)14}$	$6\overline{)30}$	$7\overline{)7}$	$8\overline{)40}$	$8\overline{)16}$

"All the rivers run into the sea." Ecclesiastes 1:7

Write the Roman numerals.

10. 19 18 20 16

11. 17 19 18 20

12. 28 ÷ 7 = 42 ÷ 7 = 21 ÷ 7 =

13. 60 ÷ 6 = 36 ÷ 4 = 55 ÷ 5 =

14. 84 ÷ 7 = 56 ÷ 7 = 72 ÷ 6 =

15. 45 ÷ 5 = 49 ÷ 7 = 63 ÷ 7 =

16. 7 ÷ 7 = 35 ÷ 7 = 14 ÷ 7 =

17. In the story of *Mary Jones and Her Bible,* Mary walked 2 miles each Saturday to read a Bible. How many miles did she walk in seven Saturdays?

18. Fifteen finches sat on a wire. $\frac{1}{2}$ dozen of them flitted away. How many finches were left on the wire?

1.	8)48	6)18	8)72	6)54	6)72
2.	5)15	7)42	5)60	5)45	7)63
3.	8)32	6)48	6)24	7)84	8)24
4.	5)20	5)40	7)28	7)21	8)96
5.	6)30	7)77	7)49	6)42	7)28
6.	8)88	5)25	8)32	5)35	8)56
7.	8)40	6)6	6)36	7)14	8)80
8.	5)30	8)8	7)35	7)70	8)16
9.	8)64	6)12	5)0	5)10	7)56

"All the rivers run into the sea." Ecclesiastes 1:7

Write the Roman numerals.

10. 20 17 18 16

11. 17 18 16 19

12. $64 \div 8 =$ $63 \div 7 =$ $42 \div 6 =$

13. $49 \div 7 =$ $54 \div 6 =$ $56 \div 7 =$

14. School children went in vans to sing at a rest home. 8 children rode in each van. There were $\frac{1}{2}$ dozen vans. How many children went to sing?

15. Grandmother is 66 years old, and Ann is nine. How much younger is Ann than Grandmother?

16. One dozen otters played together. 4 of them slid down a bank.
The rest swam.
How many
swam?

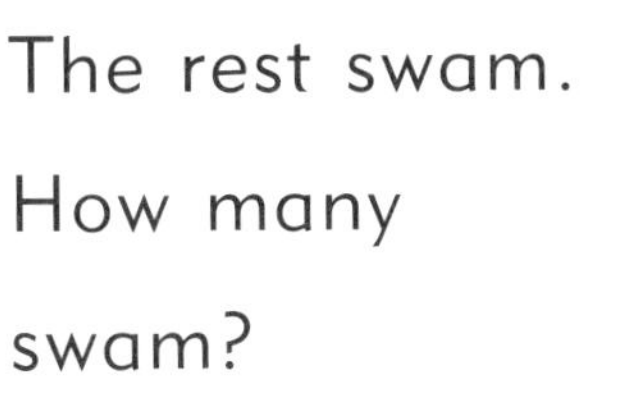

1.	$8\overline{)32}$	$6\overline{)54}$	$1\overline{)7}$	$5\overline{)45}$	$7\overline{)28}$
2.	$7\overline{)63}$	$3\overline{)27}$	$4\overline{)20}$	$2\overline{)8}$	$3\overline{)9}$
3.	$8\overline{)24}$	$8\overline{)56}$	$3\overline{)0}$	$7\overline{)49}$	$7\overline{)21}$
4.	$2\overline{)6}$	$4\overline{)16}$	$3\overline{)15}$	$4\overline{)36}$	$8\overline{)72}$
5.	$3\overline{)24}$	$8\overline{)16}$	$7\overline{)70}$	$6\overline{)48}$	$8\overline{)40}$
6.	$7\overline{)14}$	$4\overline{)32}$	$5\overline{)40}$	$8\overline{)80}$	$7\overline{)35}$
7.	$4\overline{)8}$	$7\overline{)42}$	$5\overline{)30}$	$7\overline{)84}$	$8\overline{)64}$
8.	$8\overline{)48}$	$2\overline{)4}$	$8\overline{)96}$	$6\overline{)36}$	$7\overline{)56}$
9.	$6\overline{)42}$	$4\overline{)24}$	$4\overline{)48}$	$3\overline{)18}$	$5\overline{)35}$

"All the rivers run into the sea." Ecclesiastes 1:7

10. 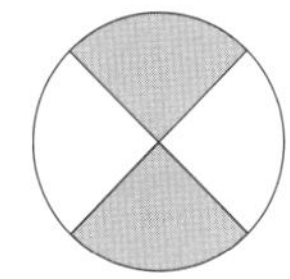 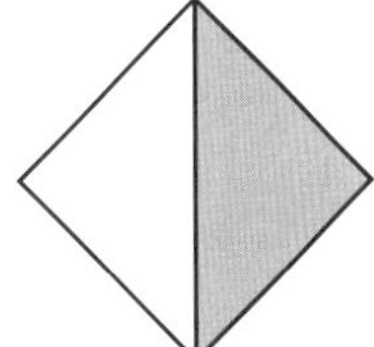 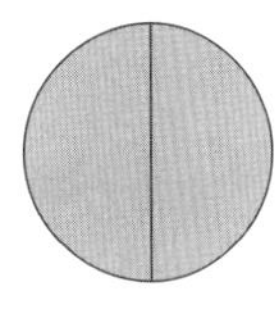

11. 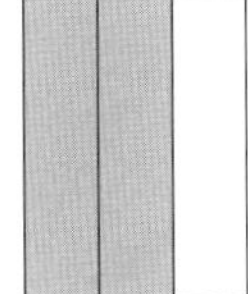 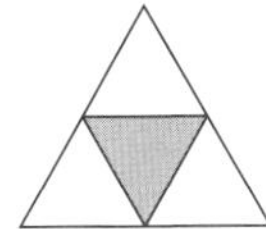 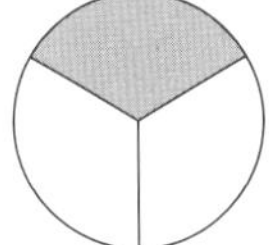 

12. 63 ÷ 7 = 84 ÷ 7 = 36 ÷ 4 =

13. 49 ÷ 7 = 56 ÷ 7 = 24 ÷ 6 =

14. 64 ÷ 8 = 36 ÷ 6 = 30 ÷ 5 =

15. 42 ÷ 6 = 28 ÷ 7 = 48 ÷ 6 =

16. 54 ÷ 6 = 72 ÷ 8 = 72 ÷ 6 =

17. The Bible tells about a man who was king for 1 year. How many months was that? *Write the rule.*

18. God sent rain every day for a week. How many days was that? *Write the rule.*

1.	$8\overline{)96}$	$4\overline{)32}$	$6\overline{)72}$	$8\overline{)48}$	$5\overline{)45}$
2.	$3\overline{)24}$	$7\overline{)84}$	$7\overline{)42}$	$5\overline{)60}$	$6\overline{)54}$
3.	$7\overline{)49}$	$6\overline{)48}$	$1\overline{)9}$	$5\overline{)40}$	$8\overline{)56}$
4.	$8\overline{)72}$	$4\overline{)36}$	$7\overline{)21}$	$5\overline{)20}$	$8\overline{)40}$
5.	$7\overline{)35}$	$6\overline{)24}$	$8\overline{)24}$	$3\overline{)27}$	$7\overline{)63}$
6.	$3\overline{)18}$	$7\overline{)56}$	$4\overline{)28}$	$8\overline{)88}$	$6\overline{)18}$
7.	$8\overline{)64}$	$4\overline{)24}$	$7\overline{)77}$	$3\overline{)21}$	$5\overline{)15}$
8.	$7\overline{)28}$	$6\overline{)30}$	$4\overline{)20}$	$5\overline{)25}$	$8\overline{)32}$
9.	$7\overline{)70}$	$6\overline{)36}$	$2\overline{)10}$	$5\overline{)30}$	$8\overline{)80}$

"All the rivers run into the sea." Ecclesiastes 1:7

Write the Roman numerals.

10. 19 17 20 16

11. 18 20 17 19

12. $8 \times 8 + 2 =$ $7 \times 10 + 3 =$

13. $6 \times 9 + 3 =$ $7 \times 7 + 1 =$

14. $5 \times 9 + 2 =$ $4 \times 11 + 3 =$

15. $8 \times 6 + 2 =$ $8 \times 7 + 1 =$

16. $8 \times 9 + 1 =$ $7 \times 9 + 3 =$

17. $7 \times 8 + 2 =$ $8 \times 5 + 3 =$

18.

$9.00	$ .97	$4.57	$9.93
+ .50	− .69	+ 2.78	− .25

19.

$ .86	$4.75	$3.29	$9.83
− .59	+ 4.74	+ 6.38	− 2.49

137

1.	0 × 9	1 × 9	2 × 9	3 × 9	4 × 9	5 × 9	6 × 9
2.	7 × 9	8 × 9	9 × 9	10 × 9	11 × 9	12 × 9	
3.	12 × 9	9 × 9	6 × 9	8 × 9	4 × 9	10 × 9	7 × 9
4.	8 × 9	3 × 9	12 × 9	9 × 9	7 × 9	11 × 9	8 × 9
5.	7 × 9	10 × 9	4 × 9	8 × 9	6 × 9	9 × 9	12 × 9
6.	8 × 9	11 × 9	7 × 9	9 × 9	12 × 9	3 × 9	8 × 9
7.	5 × 9	2 × 9	0 × 9	1 × 9	0 × 9	2 × 9	5 × 9

"The LORD shall . . . give . . . showers of rain." Zechariah 10:1

137

1.
$$\begin{array}{ccccccc} 0 & 1 & 2 & 3 & 4 & 5 & 6 \\ \times 9 & \times 9 & \times 9 & \times 9 & \times 9 & \times 9 & \times 9 \end{array}$$

2.
$$\begin{array}{cccccc} 7 & 8 & 9 & 10 & 11 & 12 \\ \times 9 & \times 9 & \times 9 & \times 9 & \times 9 & \times 9 \end{array}$$

3.
$$\begin{array}{ccccccc} 12 & 9 & 6 & 8 & 4 & 10 & 7 \\ \times 9 & \times 9 & \times 9 & \times 9 & \times 9 & \times 9 & \times 9 \end{array}$$

4.
$$\begin{array}{ccccccc} 8 & 3 & 12 & 9 & 7 & 11 & 8 \\ \times 9 & \times 9 & \times 9 & \times 9 & \times 9 & \times 9 & \times 9 \end{array}$$

5.
$$\begin{array}{ccccccc} 7 & 10 & 4 & 8 & 6 & 9 & 12 \\ \times 9 & \times 9 & \times 9 & \times 9 & \times 9 & \times 9 & \times 9 \end{array}$$

6.
$$\begin{array}{ccccccc} 8 & 11 & 7 & 9 & 12 & 3 & 8 \\ \times 9 & \times 9 & \times 9 & \times 9 & \times 9 & \times 9 & \times 9 \end{array}$$

7.
$$\begin{array}{ccccccc} 5 & 2 & 0 & 1 & 0 & 2 & 5 \\ \times 9 & \times 9 & \times 9 & \times 9 & \times 9 & \times 9 & \times 9 \end{array}$$

"The LORD shall . . . give . . . showers of rain." Zechariah 10:1

8.

9.

10.

45	23	34	63	26	35
33	56	2	21	43	50
+ 35	+ 76	+ 87	+ 87	+ 46	+ 58

11.

44	35	62	63	35	54
75	23	7	10	54	22
+ 3	+ 96	+ 43	+ 69	+ 25	+ 94

12. The longest verse in the Bible has 90 words. The shortest verse has two words. What is the difference in the number of words?

13. A greenhouse worker planted 8 tulips in each flower box. He had $\frac{1}{2}$ dozen boxes. How many tulips did he plant in all?

1.	8 × 9	6 × 9	5 × 9	8 × 9	4 × 9	10 × 9	4 × 9
2.	6 × 9	8 × 9	4 × 9	10 × 9	4 × 9	8 × 9	5 × 9
3.	7 × 9	12 × 9	1 × 9	9 × 9	6 × 9	7 × 9	2 × 9
4.	6 × 9	9 × 9	1 × 9	12 × 9	7 × 9	2 × 9	7 × 9
5.	4 × 9	12 × 9	5 × 9	11 × 9	9 × 9	7 × 9	8 × 9
6.	12 × 9	4 × 9	8 × 9	7 × 9	9 × 9	11 × 9	5 × 9
7.	3 × 9	9 × 9	6 × 9	0 × 9	6 × 9	9 × 9	3 × 9

"The LORD shall . . . give . . . showers of rain." Zechariah 10:1

1.
$$\begin{array}{r} 8 \\ \times 9 \\ \hline \end{array}\quad \begin{array}{r} 6 \\ \times 9 \\ \hline \end{array}\quad \begin{array}{r} 5 \\ \times 9 \\ \hline \end{array}\quad \begin{array}{r} 8 \\ \times 9 \\ \hline \end{array}\quad \begin{array}{r} 4 \\ \times 9 \\ \hline \end{array}\quad \begin{array}{r} 10 \\ \times 9 \\ \hline \end{array}\quad \begin{array}{r} 4 \\ \times 9 \\ \hline \end{array}$$

2.
$$\begin{array}{r} 6 \\ \times 9 \\ \hline \end{array}\quad \begin{array}{r} 8 \\ \times 9 \\ \hline \end{array}\quad \begin{array}{r} 4 \\ \times 9 \\ \hline \end{array}\quad \begin{array}{r} 10 \\ \times 9 \\ \hline \end{array}\quad \begin{array}{r} 4 \\ \times 9 \\ \hline \end{array}\quad \begin{array}{r} 8 \\ \times 9 \\ \hline \end{array}\quad \begin{array}{r} 5 \\ \times 9 \\ \hline \end{array}$$

3.
$$\begin{array}{r} 7 \\ \times 9 \\ \hline \end{array}\quad \begin{array}{r} 12 \\ \times 9 \\ \hline \end{array}\quad \begin{array}{r} 1 \\ \times 9 \\ \hline \end{array}\quad \begin{array}{r} 9 \\ \times 9 \\ \hline \end{array}\quad \begin{array}{r} 6 \\ \times 9 \\ \hline \end{array}\quad \begin{array}{r} 7 \\ \times 9 \\ \hline \end{array}\quad \begin{array}{r} 2 \\ \times 9 \\ \hline \end{array}$$

4.
$$\begin{array}{r} 6 \\ \times 9 \\ \hline \end{array}\quad \begin{array}{r} 9 \\ \times 9 \\ \hline \end{array}\quad \begin{array}{r} 1 \\ \times 9 \\ \hline \end{array}\quad \begin{array}{r} 12 \\ \times 9 \\ \hline \end{array}\quad \begin{array}{r} 7 \\ \times 9 \\ \hline \end{array}\quad \begin{array}{r} 2 \\ \times 9 \\ \hline \end{array}\quad \begin{array}{r} 7 \\ \times 9 \\ \hline \end{array}$$

5.
$$\begin{array}{r} 4 \\ \times 9 \\ \hline \end{array}\quad \begin{array}{r} 12 \\ \times 9 \\ \hline \end{array}\quad \begin{array}{r} 5 \\ \times 9 \\ \hline \end{array}\quad \begin{array}{r} 11 \\ \times 9 \\ \hline \end{array}\quad \begin{array}{r} 9 \\ \times 9 \\ \hline \end{array}\quad \begin{array}{r} 7 \\ \times 9 \\ \hline \end{array}\quad \begin{array}{r} 8 \\ \times 9 \\ \hline \end{array}$$

6.
$$\begin{array}{r} 12 \\ \times 9 \\ \hline \end{array}\quad \begin{array}{r} 4 \\ \times 9 \\ \hline \end{array}\quad \begin{array}{r} 8 \\ \times 9 \\ \hline \end{array}\quad \begin{array}{r} 7 \\ \times 9 \\ \hline \end{array}\quad \begin{array}{r} 9 \\ \times 9 \\ \hline \end{array}\quad \begin{array}{r} 11 \\ \times 9 \\ \hline \end{array}\quad \begin{array}{r} 5 \\ \times 9 \\ \hline \end{array}$$

7.
$$\begin{array}{r} 3 \\ \times 9 \\ \hline \end{array}\quad \begin{array}{r} 9 \\ \times 9 \\ \hline \end{array}\quad \begin{array}{r} 6 \\ \times 9 \\ \hline \end{array}\quad \begin{array}{r} 0 \\ \times 9 \\ \hline \end{array}\quad \begin{array}{r} 6 \\ \times 9 \\ \hline \end{array}\quad \begin{array}{r} 9 \\ \times 9 \\ \hline \end{array}\quad \begin{array}{r} 3 \\ \times 9 \\ \hline \end{array}$$

"The LORD shall . . . give . . . showers of rain." Zechariah 10:1

8.	566 - 398	932 - 584	635 - 266	737 - 488	934 - 299
9.	925 - 677	921 - 553	826 - 479	634 - 467	821 - 187

10. Melvin has a penny that is 40 years old and a dime that is 26 years old. How many years older is the penny than the dime?

11. 8 spring peepers sat on each tree. How many peepers sat on $\frac{1}{2}$ dozen trees?

12. God made a sweet song for the spring peeper to sing. Fern's family sat on the porch steps to hear the song. 2 people sat on each step. There were 7 steps. How many people was that?

1.	6×9	8×9	5×9	12×9	5×9	8×9	6×9
2.	4×9	10×9	9×9	11×9	9×9	7×9	11×9
3.	9×9	11×9	9×9	10×9	4×9	11×9	7×9
4.	8×9	3×9	5×9	9×9	12×9	1×9	6×9
5.	3×9	8×9	6×9	1×9	12×9	9×9	5×9
6.	8×9	0×9	4×9	10×9	4×9	0×9	8×9
7.	2×9	7×9	3×9	9×9	3×9	7×9	2×9

"The LORD shall . . . give . . . showers of rain." Zechariah 10:1

Write the Roman numerals.

8. 17 18 20 19

9. 18 20 19 16

10. nine thousand, eight hundred ninety

11. seven thousand, six hundred eighty

12. six thousand, twenty-seven

13. eight thousand, thirty-six

14. seven thousand, four hundred fifty

15. nine thousand, two hundred forty

16.

934	923	622	854	875
- 375	- 256	- 246	- 589	- 687

17.

752	833	844	986	923
- 377	- 167	- 286	- 799	- 659

1.	10×9	12×9	9×8	5×9	9×8	7×8	11×9
2.	4×9	9×9	7×9	7×8	8×8	6×8	6×9
3.	10×9	7×8	9×8	5×9	8×9	12×9	11×9
4.	4×9	6×8	8×8	7×8	7×9	9×9	6×9
5.	6×8	4×8	4×9	5×7	4×9	4×8	6×8

6.	$6\overline{)366}$	$6\overline{)480}$	$7\overline{)567}$	$3\overline{)276}$
7.	$8\overline{)640}$	$8\overline{)568}$	$2\overline{)184}$	$5\overline{)455}$

"The LORD shall . . . give . . . showers of rain." Zechariah 10:1

8. 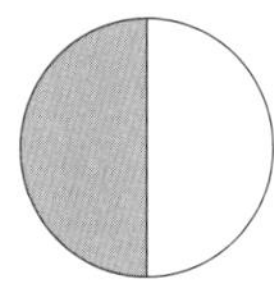 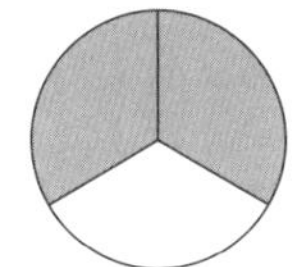 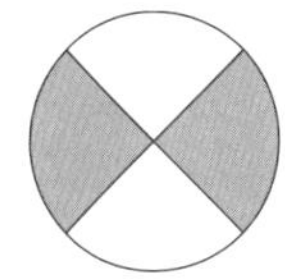

9. 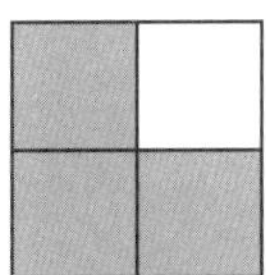 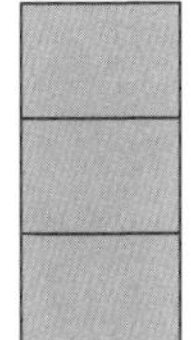 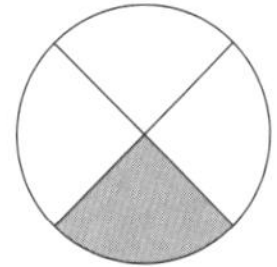 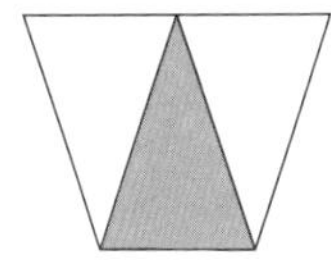

10. $\frac{1}{2}$ of 18 $\frac{1}{4}$ of 32 $\frac{1}{3}$ of 36

11. $\frac{1}{4}$ of 28 $\frac{1}{3}$ of 18 $\frac{1}{4}$ of 20

12. $\frac{1}{2}$ of 10 $\frac{1}{4}$ of 24 $\frac{1}{2}$ of 14

13. $\frac{1}{4}$ of 48 $\frac{1}{3}$ of 24 $\frac{1}{3}$ of 27

14. A calendar shows 12 months. How many years is that? *Write the rule.*

15. A spring peeper sang in a tree 36 inches above the ground. How many yards was that? *Write the rule.*

16. Susan's family planted 1 pound of beans in the garden. How many ounces was that? *Write the rule.*

1. $\begin{array}{r}8\\ \times 9\\ \hline\end{array}$ $\begin{array}{r}9\\ \times 9\\ \hline\end{array}$ $\begin{array}{r}6\\ \times 9\\ \hline\end{array}$ $\begin{array}{r}4\\ \times 9\\ \hline\end{array}$ $\begin{array}{r}6\\ \times 7\\ \hline\end{array}$ $\begin{array}{r}12\\ \times 8\\ \hline\end{array}$ $\begin{array}{r}5\\ \times 9\\ \hline\end{array}$

2. $\begin{array}{r}7\\ \times 8\\ \hline\end{array}$ $\begin{array}{r}6\\ \times 8\\ \hline\end{array}$ $\begin{array}{r}12\\ \times 9\\ \hline\end{array}$ $\begin{array}{r}3\\ \times 9\\ \hline\end{array}$ $\begin{array}{r}8\\ \times 8\\ \hline\end{array}$ $\begin{array}{r}4\\ \times 8\\ \hline\end{array}$ $\begin{array}{r}7\\ \times 7\\ \hline\end{array}$

3. $\begin{array}{r}7\\ \times 9\\ \hline\end{array}$ $\begin{array}{r}5\\ \times 8\\ \hline\end{array}$ $\begin{array}{r}4\\ \times 7\\ \hline\end{array}$ $\begin{array}{r}12\\ \times 7\\ \hline\end{array}$ $\begin{array}{r}4\\ \times 7\\ \hline\end{array}$ $\begin{array}{r}5\\ \times 8\\ \hline\end{array}$ $\begin{array}{r}9\\ \times 7\\ \hline\end{array}$

4. $\begin{array}{r}8\\ \times 7\\ \hline\end{array}$ $\begin{array}{r}4\\ \times 8\\ \hline\end{array}$ $\begin{array}{r}8\\ \times 8\\ \hline\end{array}$ $\begin{array}{r}3\\ \times 9\\ \hline\end{array}$ $\begin{array}{r}12\\ \times 9\\ \hline\end{array}$ $\begin{array}{r}6\\ \times 8\\ \hline\end{array}$ $\begin{array}{r}7\\ \times 7\\ \hline\end{array}$

5. $\begin{array}{r}9\\ \times 8\\ \hline\end{array}$ $\begin{array}{r}12\\ \times 8\\ \hline\end{array}$ $\begin{array}{r}6\\ \times 7\\ \hline\end{array}$ $\begin{array}{r}4\\ \times 9\\ \hline\end{array}$ $\begin{array}{r}6\\ \times 9\\ \hline\end{array}$ $\begin{array}{r}9\\ \times 9\\ \hline\end{array}$ $\begin{array}{r}5\\ \times 9\\ \hline\end{array}$

6. $2\overline{)184}$ $8\overline{)240}$ $7\overline{)217}$ $3\overline{)279}$

7. $4\overline{)168}$ $5\overline{)250}$ $6\overline{)306}$ $3\overline{)129}$

"The LORD shall . . . give . . . showers of rain." Zechariah 10:1

8.

827	635	622	936	935
- 358	- 478	- 357	- 358	- 299

9.

942	554	937	821	851
- 678	- 398	- 469	- 186	- 274

10. 1 half dollar + 2 quarters   1 dollar + 10 dimes

11. 7 dollars + 10 nickels   1 half dollar + 3 quarters

12. 9 dimes + 13 nickels   1 half dollar + 9 nickels

13. 1 dollar + 4 quarters   1 dollar + 2 half dollars

14. $63 \div 7 =$ $32 \div 8 =$ $49 \div 7 =$

15. $24 \div 6 =$ $72 \div 8 =$ $42 \div 6 =$

142

1.
7	8	9	12	6	12	9
× 9	× 9	× 6	× 9	× 9	× 6	× 9

2.
8	8	7	7	12	8	6
× 8	× 9	× 6	× 7	× 8	× 7	× 6

3.
10	6	9	11	7	12	10
× 8	× 7	× 8	× 9	× 8	× 8	× 9

4.
8	6	4	7	2	4	4
× 8	× 8	× 8	× 7	× 9	× 6	× 9

5.
9	4	8	12	3	3	9
× 9	× 8	× 6	× 9	× 8	× 6	× 7

6. $3\overline{)249}$ $5\overline{)450}$ $7\overline{)637}$ $2\overline{)168}$

7. $7\overline{)497}$ $4\overline{)328}$ $2\overline{)166}$ $3\overline{)216}$

"The LORD shall . . . give . . . showers of rain." Zechariah 10:1

8.

52	63	33	52	33	54
96	24	20	7	52	35
+ 7	+ 39	+ 46	+ 78	+ 66	+ 85

9.

72	33	43	90	35	24
45	45	26	5	44	32
+ 8	+ 76	+ 67	+ 3	+ 94	+ 94

10. Ray's big brother led 4 songs on Sunday morning. In the evening he led 3 times as many. How many songs did he lead in the evening?

11. Mother's red tulips had 7 buds. Her yellow tulips had 8 times as many. How many buds did the yellow tulips have?

12. 7 spring peepers clung to rushes. Six times as many hopped into the pond. How many peepers hopped into the pond?

1.	8 × 9	12 × 5	4 × 9	0 × 1	6 × 6	10 × 6	12 × 9
2.	6 × 9	9 × 8	8 × 4	12 × 1	5 × 9	8 × 8	12 × 3
3.	9 × 6	9 × 5	2 × 6	4 × 8	8 × 9	9 × 4	8 × 8
4.	9 × 9	3 × 6	5 × 6	9 × 7	12 × 2	3 × 7	7 × 8
5.	2 × 9	9 × 9	7 × 3	3 × 8	7 × 9	6 × 5	8 × 7
6.	6 × 7	12 × 4	3 × 3	10 × 9	9 × 1	6 × 8	7 × 6
7.	12 × 9	5 × 8	5 × 4	11 × 9	4 × 5	10 × 4	12 × 6

"The LORD shall . . . give . . . showers of rain." Zechariah 10:1

143

1.
$$\begin{array}{r} 8 \\ \times 9 \end{array}\qquad \begin{array}{r} 12 \\ \times 5 \end{array}\qquad \begin{array}{r} 4 \\ \times 9 \end{array}\qquad \begin{array}{r} 0 \\ \times 1 \end{array}\qquad \begin{array}{r} 6 \\ \times 6 \end{array}\qquad \begin{array}{r} 10 \\ \times 6 \end{array}\qquad \begin{array}{r} 12 \\ \times 9 \end{array}$$

2.
$$\begin{array}{r} 6 \\ \times 9 \end{array}\qquad \begin{array}{r} 9 \\ \times 8 \end{array}\qquad \begin{array}{r} 8 \\ \times 4 \end{array}\qquad \begin{array}{r} 12 \\ \times 1 \end{array}\qquad \begin{array}{r} 5 \\ \times 9 \end{array}\qquad \begin{array}{r} 8 \\ \times 8 \end{array}\qquad \begin{array}{r} 12 \\ \times 3 \end{array}$$

3.
$$\begin{array}{r} 9 \\ \times 6 \end{array}\qquad \begin{array}{r} 9 \\ \times 5 \end{array}\qquad \begin{array}{r} 2 \\ \times 6 \end{array}\qquad \begin{array}{r} 4 \\ \times 8 \end{array}\qquad \begin{array}{r} 8 \\ \times 9 \end{array}\qquad \begin{array}{r} 9 \\ \times 4 \end{array}\qquad \begin{array}{r} 8 \\ \times 8 \end{array}$$

4.
$$\begin{array}{r} 9 \\ \times 9 \end{array}\qquad \begin{array}{r} 3 \\ \times 6 \end{array}\qquad \begin{array}{r} 5 \\ \times 6 \end{array}\qquad \begin{array}{r} 9 \\ \times 7 \end{array}\qquad \begin{array}{r} 12 \\ \times 2 \end{array}\qquad \begin{array}{r} 3 \\ \times 7 \end{array}\qquad \begin{array}{r} 7 \\ \times 8 \end{array}$$

5.
$$\begin{array}{r} 2 \\ \times 9 \end{array}\qquad \begin{array}{r} 9 \\ \times 9 \end{array}\qquad \begin{array}{r} 7 \\ \times 3 \end{array}\qquad \begin{array}{r} 3 \\ \times 8 \end{array}\qquad \begin{array}{r} 7 \\ \times 9 \end{array}\qquad \begin{array}{r} 6 \\ \times 5 \end{array}\qquad \begin{array}{r} 8 \\ \times 7 \end{array}$$

6.
$$\begin{array}{r} 6 \\ \times 7 \end{array}\qquad \begin{array}{r} 12 \\ \times 4 \end{array}\qquad \begin{array}{r} 3 \\ \times 3 \end{array}\qquad \begin{array}{r} 10 \\ \times 9 \end{array}\qquad \begin{array}{r} 9 \\ \times 1 \end{array}\qquad \begin{array}{r} 6 \\ \times 8 \end{array}\qquad \begin{array}{r} 7 \\ \times 6 \end{array}$$

7.
$$\begin{array}{r} 12 \\ \times 9 \end{array}\qquad \begin{array}{r} 5 \\ \times 8 \end{array}\qquad \begin{array}{r} 5 \\ \times 4 \end{array}\qquad \begin{array}{r} 11 \\ \times 9 \end{array}\qquad \begin{array}{r} 4 \\ \times 5 \end{array}\qquad \begin{array}{r} 10 \\ \times 4 \end{array}\qquad \begin{array}{r} 12 \\ \times 6 \end{array}$$

"The LORD shall . . . give . . . showers of rain." Zechariah 10:1

8.

964	922	986	837	723
- 378	- 254	- 598	- 599	- 267

9.

952	526	626	765	853
- 497	- 289	- 239	- 98	- 268

10. $6 \times 9 + 3 =$ $\quad$ $8 \times 9 + 2 =$

11. $9 \times 7 + 3 =$ $\quad$ $7 \times 9 + 2 =$

12. $6 \times 12 + 2 =$ $\quad$ $8 \times 7 + 1 =$

13. $6 \times 8 + 2 =$ $\quad$ $4 \times 12 + 1 =$

14. The Bible says that Noah had 3 sons. Jacob had 4 times as many. How many sons did Jacob have?

15. 85 insects buzzed around a spring peeper. The peeper ate 49 of them. How many insects were not eaten?

1. 8×9 7×9 12×4 8×8 9×5 5×8 9×9

2. 12×3 6×8 9×7 8×5 5×9 8×8 8×7

3. 4×9 12×9 6×9 12×2 7×6 3×3 7×8

4. 9×8 3×8 9×6 12×9 9×1 6×7 9×9

5. $8\overline{)72}$ $7\overline{)49}$ $8\overline{)40}$ $7\overline{)77}$ $7\overline{)84}$

6. $8\overline{)64}$ $7\overline{)42}$ $8\overline{)32}$ $7\overline{)21}$ $6\overline{)60}$

7. $8\overline{)96}$ $6\overline{)66}$ $7\overline{)35}$ $8\overline{)56}$ $7\overline{)63}$

8. $8\overline{)80}$ $6\overline{)18}$ $7\overline{)28}$ $8\overline{)48}$ $7\overline{)56}$

"The LORD shall . . . give . . . showers of rain." Zechariah 10:1

Write the Roman numerals.

9. 19 16 18 17

10. 16 18 17 20

11. nine thousand, fifty-eight

12. seven thousand, three hundred five

13. five thousand, thirty-seven

14. eight thousand, five hundred nine

15. four thousand, two hundred seventy-five

16. nine thousand, five hundred seventy-two

17. Dawn's baby sister is 1 year old. How many months is that? *Write the rule.*

18. Father waited for 365 days to see his dogwood tree bloom. How many years was that? *Write the rule.*

1. $9\overline{)0}$ $9\overline{)9}$ $9\overline{)18}$ $9\overline{)27}$ $9\overline{)36}$

2. $9\overline{)45}$ $9\overline{)54}$ $9\overline{)63}$ $9\overline{)72}$ $9\overline{)81}$

3. $9\overline{)90}$ $9\overline{)99}$ $9\overline{)108}$

4. $9\overline{)72}$ $9\overline{)108}$ $9\overline{)63}$ $9\overline{)9}$ $9\overline{)99}$

5. $9\overline{)9}$ $9\overline{)63}$ $9\overline{)108}$ $9\overline{)72}$ $9\overline{)54}$

6. $9\overline{)81}$ $9\overline{)45}$ $9\overline{)81}$ $9\overline{)27}$ $9\overline{)36}$

7. $9\overline{)45}$ $9\overline{)81}$ $9\overline{)27}$ $9\overline{)81}$ $9\overline{)36}$

8. $9\overline{)90}$ $9\overline{)18}$ $9\overline{)0}$ $9\overline{)108}$ $9\overline{)54}$

9. $9\overline{)108}$ $9\overline{)0}$ $9\overline{)18}$ $9\overline{)90}$ $9\overline{)99}$

"I will sing of thy power." Psalm 59:16

10.

$8.64	$5.73	$9.69	$9.50
- 5.35	+ 2.64	- 3.80	- 7.99

11.

$9.74	$8.47	$3.29	$3.47
- 6.46	- 6.97	+ 2.59	+ 4.89

12. 56 ÷ 8 = 48 ÷ 4 = 64 ÷ 8 =

13. 49 ÷ 7 = 56 ÷ 7 = 28 ÷ 7 =

14. 50 ÷ 5 = 36 ÷ 6 = 24 ÷ 4 =

15. 28 ÷ 4 = 32 ÷ 8 = 48 ÷ 6 =

16. 42 ÷ 6 = 40 ÷ 5 = 96 ÷ 8 =

17. Mother dumped 2 cups of milk into the soup that she was stirring. How many pints was that? *Write the rule.*

18. Father dipped his brush into 1 pint of blue paint. How many cups was that? *Write the rule.*

1.	$9\overline{)108}$	$9\overline{)72}$	$9\overline{)45}$	$9\overline{)27}$	$9\overline{)90}$
2.	$9\overline{)54}$	$9\overline{)27}$	$9\overline{)45}$	$9\overline{)72}$	$9\overline{)63}$
3.	$9\overline{)81}$	$9\overline{)36}$	$9\overline{)0}$	$9\overline{)36}$	$9\overline{)81}$
4.	$9\overline{)54}$	$9\overline{)9}$	$9\overline{)63}$	$9\overline{)18}$	$9\overline{)63}$
5.	$9\overline{)108}$	$9\overline{)18}$	$9\overline{)63}$	$9\overline{)9}$	$9\overline{)90}$
6.	617×3	893×3	915×6	703×8	432×4
7.	705×7	882×3	980×4	713×6	951×6
8.	926×3	624×4	792×2	841×7	705×5

"I will sing of thy power." Psalm 59:16

9.  

10.  

11. $\frac{1}{4}$ of 36 $\qquad$ $\frac{1}{3}$ of 12 $\qquad$ $\frac{1}{3}$ of 24

12. $\frac{1}{2}$ of 14 $\qquad$ $\frac{1}{2}$ of 18 $\qquad$ $\frac{1}{4}$ of 28

13. $\frac{1}{4}$ of 32 $\qquad$ $\frac{1}{4}$ of 16 $\qquad$ $\frac{1}{3}$ of 27

14. Fay sifted 2 cups of flour for Mother to make bread. How many pints was that? *Write the rule.*

15. From the Bible we know that King Solomon's throne had $\frac{1}{2}$ dozen steps. How many steps was that? *Write the rule.*

1. $9\overline{)99}$ $9\overline{)54}$ $9\overline{)36}$ $9\overline{)27}$ $9\overline{)90}$

2. $9\overline{)9}$ $9\overline{)36}$ $9\overline{)54}$ $9\overline{)18}$ $9\overline{)45}$

3. $9\overline{)63}$ $9\overline{)72}$ $9\overline{)108}$ $9\overline{)72}$ $9\overline{)63}$

4. $9\overline{)9}$ $9\overline{)63}$ $9\overline{)81}$ $9\overline{)18}$ $9\overline{)45}$

5. $9\overline{)99}$ $9\overline{)81}$ $9\overline{)63}$ $9\overline{)27}$ $9\overline{)90}$

6. 841×8 961×6 942×4 729×3 704×7

7. 946×2 608×4 931×8 608×4 915×5

8. 520×8 850×7 603×6 319×4 329×3

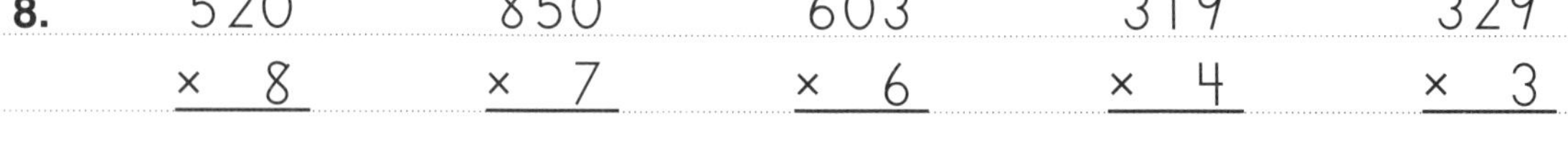

"I will sing of thy power." Psalm 59:16

Write the Roman numerals.

9. 20 15 17 19

10. 14 16 18 20

11. $56 \div 8 =$ $40 \div 8 =$ $21 \div 3 =$

12. There are 130 pages in *The Man in Bearskin.* Father read 87 of the pages to the family. How many pages has he yet to read?

13. 2 inches of rain fell in March. In April three times as many inches fell. How many inches of rain fell in April?

14. 5 lily pads were empty. Four times as many held spring peepers. How many lily pads held spring peepers?

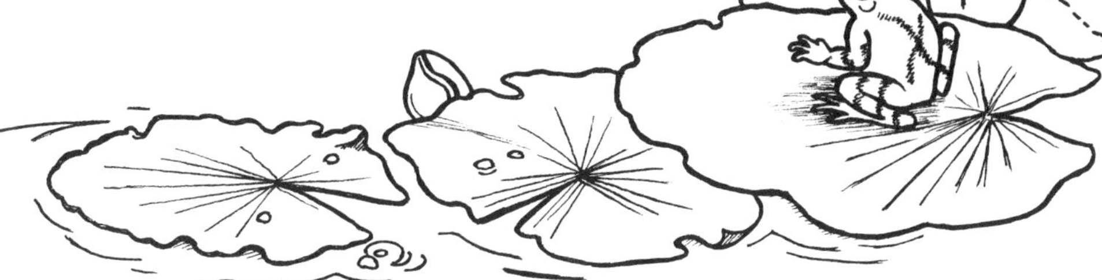

1.	$9\overline{)81}$	$9\overline{)54}$	$9\overline{)0}$	$8\overline{)48}$	$8\overline{)72}$
2.	$9\overline{)108}$	$9\overline{)45}$	$9\overline{)36}$	$9\overline{)81}$	$9\overline{)63}$
3.	$8\overline{)64}$	$8\overline{)24}$	$9\overline{)99}$	$8\overline{)8}$	$9\overline{)18}$
4.	$8\overline{)56}$	$8\overline{)72}$	$8\overline{)32}$	$8\overline{)40}$	$8\overline{)96}$
5.	$8\overline{)16}$	$9\overline{)9}$	$8\overline{)88}$	$9\overline{)27}$	$9\overline{)72}$

6.	814×7	693×3	904×8	592×4	916×6
7.	783×2	813×5	627×3	905×5	640×7
8.	705×7	940×8	246×2	862×4	930×7

"I will sing of thy power." Psalm 59:16

9. 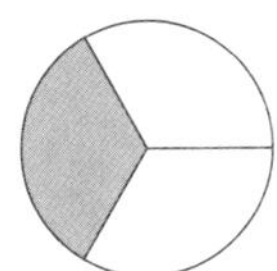 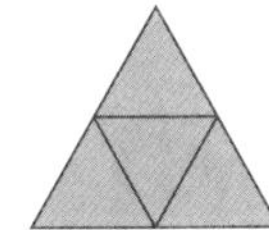 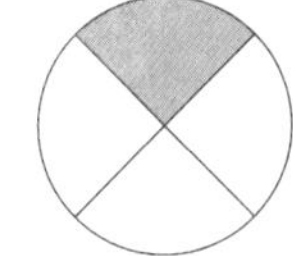 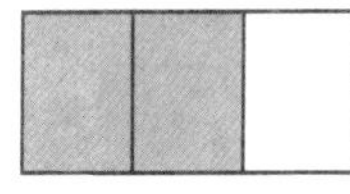

10. 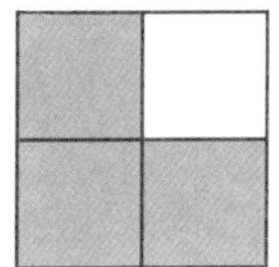 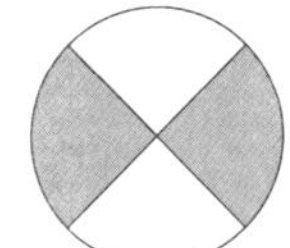 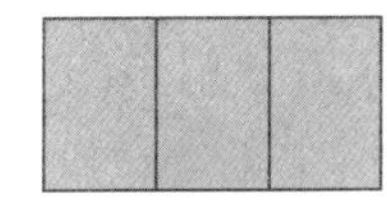 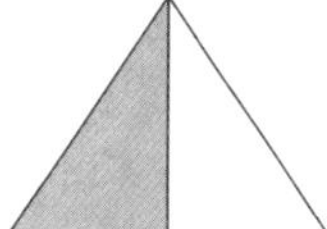

11.

955	605	426	927	833
- 367	- 548	+ 339	- 779	- 278

12.

620	489	743	843	652
- 564	+ 98	- 596	- 79	- 98

13. Rose shook 1 pint of cream until it became butter. How many cups was that? *Write the rule.*

14. Mother's flower box is 1 yard long. How many inches is that? *Write the rule.*

15. In the Bible, Paul stayed at Troas 1 week. How many days was that? *Write the rule.*

1.	$9\overline{)72}$	$9\overline{)108}$	$8\overline{)72}$	$7\overline{)42}$	$8\overline{)56}$
2.	$9\overline{)45}$	$7\overline{)28}$	$7\overline{)35}$	$8\overline{)32}$	$8\overline{)40}$
3.	$8\overline{)64}$	$7\overline{)84}$	$9\overline{)81}$	$9\overline{)54}$	$7\overline{)49}$
4.	$9\overline{)90}$	$9\overline{)27}$	$7\overline{)70}$	$8\overline{)24}$	$8\overline{)80}$
5.	$7\overline{)56}$	$8\overline{)96}$	$7\overline{)63}$	$8\overline{)48}$	$9\overline{)63}$

6.	$4\overline{)424}$	$3\overline{)627}$	$5\overline{)515}$	$2\overline{)612}$
7.	$7\overline{)749}$	$6\overline{)618}$	$2\overline{)418}$	$3\overline{)327}$
8.	$3\overline{)918}$	$8\overline{)856}$	$4\overline{)436}$	$3\overline{)318}$
9.	$8\overline{)832}$	$3\overline{)621}$	$6\overline{)624}$	$2\overline{)414}$

"I will sing of thy power." Psalm 59:16

10.  

11.  

12. $\frac{1}{4}$ of 36 $\frac{1}{2}$ of 24 $\frac{1}{2}$ of 18

13. $\frac{1}{3}$ of 36 $\frac{1}{3}$ of 27 $\frac{1}{4}$ of 32

14. $\frac{1}{3}$ of 15 $\frac{1}{3}$ of 24 $\frac{1}{2}$ of 14

15. In the Bible, the Book of Ruth has 4 chapters. Acts has 7 times as many chapters. How many chapters are in the Book of Acts?

16. Mother mended fifteen socks. Janet mended $\frac{1}{2}$ dozen. How many more socks did Mother mend than Janet?

1.	9)108	8)64	7)28	9)81	6)42
2.	9)45	6)72	7)49	9)90	9)54
3.	7)63	6)48	9)18	7)56	6)54
4.	6)30	6)60	8)56	7)84	7)42
5.	8)96	8)72	9)36	9)72	9)63

6.	6)612	3)918	8)848	8)864
7.	5)545	7)742	2)612	3)924
8.	6)648	6)654	2)616	7)714
9.	3)621	5)530	8)856	4)828

"I will sing of thy power." Psalm 59:16

Write the Roman numerals.

10. 19 15 17 19

11. 14 16 18 20

12. 2 half dollars + 11 nickels

1 quarter + 13 nickels

13. 5 dollars + 7 nickels

3 quarters + 8 dimes

14. 1 half dollar + 89 pennies

2 quarters + 9 nickels

15. Milton helped his sister to pick 2 pints of strawberries. How many quarts was that? *Write the rule.*

16. Mother set 1 quart of milk on the breakfast table to eat with oatmeal. How many pints was that? *Write the rule.*

151

1. $9\overline{)81}$ $8\overline{)64}$ $7\overline{)63}$ $6\overline{)42}$ $7\overline{)28}$

2. $9\overline{)72}$ $8\overline{)72}$ $9\overline{)54}$ $8\overline{)24}$ $9\overline{)18}$

3. $8\overline{)40}$ $7\overline{)56}$ $9\overline{)36}$ $7\overline{)49}$ $6\overline{)54}$

4. $6\overline{)48}$ $9\overline{)45}$ $8\overline{)16}$ $9\overline{)27}$ $8\overline{)48}$

5. $8\overline{)56}$ $7\overline{)42}$ $9\overline{)99}$ $6\overline{)36}$ $9\overline{)63}$

6. $3\overline{)615}$ $8\overline{)816}$ $5\overline{)545}$ $8\overline{)872}$

7. $2\overline{)614}$ $4\overline{)436}$ $5\overline{)510}$ $8\overline{)864}$

8. $7\overline{)763}$ $3\overline{)921}$ $2\overline{)216}$ $2\overline{)410}$

9. $6\overline{)654}$ $3\overline{)324}$ $4\overline{)428}$ $7\overline{)742}$

10.

\$9.86	\$7.79	\$3.74	\$9.78
− 5.59	− .87	+ .98	− 3.49

11. $18 - 9 + 8 =$ $\qquad$ $13 - 6 + 8 =$

12. $16 - 9 + 7 =$ $\qquad$ $14 - 5 + 4 =$

13. $12 - 4 + 5 =$ $\qquad$ $15 - 6 + 5 =$

14. $17 - 8 + 6 =$ $\qquad$ $15 - 7 + 9 =$

15. $13 - 8 + 9 =$ $\qquad$ $15 - 8 + 7 =$

16. $11 - 5 + 8 =$

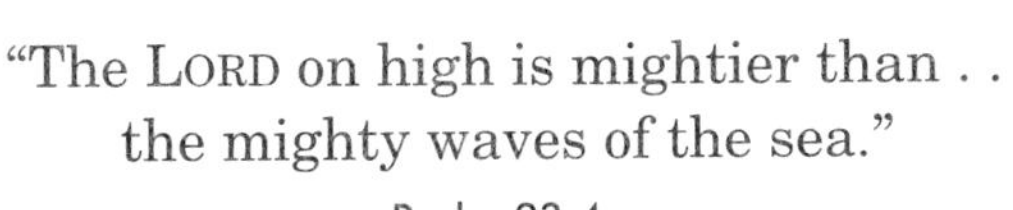
"The LORD on high is mightier than . . .
the mighty waves of the sea."

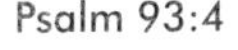
Psalm 93:4

1.	$9\overline{)63}$	$6\overline{)30}$	$4\overline{)36}$	$5\overline{)45}$	$7\overline{)56}$
2.	$4\overline{)32}$	$9\overline{)45}$	$6\overline{)54}$	$4\overline{)48}$	$8\overline{)72}$
3.	$8\overline{)40}$	$3\overline{)24}$	$6\overline{)72}$	$7\overline{)63}$	$9\overline{)81}$
4.	$6\overline{)48}$	$4\overline{)36}$	$3\overline{)27}$	$7\overline{)35}$	$8\overline{)56}$
5.	$4\overline{)32}$	$3\overline{)18}$	$8\overline{)96}$	$3\overline{)12}$	$7\overline{)49}$
6.	$1\overline{)6}$	$5\overline{)40}$	$4\overline{)16}$	$9\overline{)108}$	$6\overline{)42}$
7.	$8\overline{)48}$	$5\overline{)35}$	$1\overline{)9}$	$9\overline{)18}$	$4\overline{)28}$
8.	$8\overline{)64}$	$7\overline{)42}$	$6\overline{)60}$	$6\overline{)36}$	$9\overline{)72}$
9.	$3\overline{)21}$	$8\overline{)16}$	$2\overline{)18}$	$4\overline{)28}$	$9\overline{)54}$

"I will sing of thy power." Psalm 59:16

10.

11.

12. 56 ÷ 8 = 40 ÷ 8 = 42 ÷ 7 =

13. 63 ÷ 7 = 84 ÷ 7 = 54 ÷ 6 =

14. 36 ÷ 6 = 35 ÷ 7 = 49 ÷ 7 =

15. 32 ÷ 4 = 48 ÷ 4 = 60 ÷ 5 =

16. When Henry milked the goat, he got 2 pints of milk. How many quarts was that? *Write the rule.*

17. Grandfather's car needed 1 quart of oil. How many pints was that? *Write the rule.*

1. $2\overline{)3}$ with worked example: 1 R 1; -2; 1 $2\overline{)7}$ $2\overline{)13}$ $2\overline{)5}$

2. $2\overline{)11}$ $2\overline{)17}$ $2\overline{)15}$ $2\overline{)9}$

3. $2\overline{)13}$ $2\overline{)7}$ $2\overline{)3}$ $2\overline{)5}$

4. $2\overline{)15}$ $2\overline{)17}$ $2\overline{)11}$ $2\overline{)19}$

5. 9×9 8×8 8×7 7×7 6×6 4×7 12×9

6. 7×9 10×8 8×6 11×5 3×9 7×5 10×8

"Praise the LORD . . . all deeps." Psalm 148:7

7.

586	909	505	724	972
- 298	- 377	- 328	- 489	- 90

8.

1 half dollar
+ 2 quarters

1 quarter
+ 11 nickels

9.

3 quarters
+ 7 nickels

3 quarters
+ 87 pennies

10.

4 quarters
+ 10 dimes

8 dollars
+ 2 half dollars

11.

3 dollars
+ 2 half dollars

9 dollars
+ 9 nickels

12. Mother made 1 quart of cherry ice cream. How many pints was that? *Write the rule.*

13. Susan made a doll quilt that was 1 yard long. How many inches was that? *Write the rule.*

154

1. $3\overline{)7}$ $3\overline{)29}$ $3\overline{)23}$ $3\overline{)14}$

2. $3\overline{)17}$ $3\overline{)22}$ $3\overline{)28}$ $3\overline{)8}$

3. $2\overline{)11}$ $3\overline{)26}$ $3\overline{)11}$ $2\overline{)5}$

4. $2\overline{)5}$ $3\overline{)10}$ $3\overline{)25}$ $3\overline{)13}$

5. 6×6 8×9 9×9 8×4 8×9 7×8 12×4

6. 4×8 9×8 8×7 6×8 2×9 3×9 7×9

"Praise the LORD . . . all deeps." Psalm 148:7

7.

$$\begin{array}{r}35\\83\\+\ 6\\\hline\end{array}\qquad\begin{array}{r}46\\23\\+\ 59\\\hline\end{array}\qquad\begin{array}{r}47\\2\\+\ 96\\\hline\end{array}\qquad\begin{array}{r}22\\36\\+\ 88\\\hline\end{array}\qquad\begin{array}{r}53\\21\\+\ 55\\\hline\end{array}\qquad\begin{array}{r}44\\2\\+\ 79\\\hline\end{array}$$

8. $\frac{1}{3}$ of 24 $\qquad$ $\frac{1}{4}$ of 24 $\qquad$ $\frac{1}{4}$ of 32

9. $\frac{1}{3}$ of 18 $\qquad$ $\frac{1}{2}$ of 16 $\qquad$ $\frac{1}{2}$ of 12

10. $\frac{1}{3}$ of 36 $\qquad$ $\frac{1}{4}$ of 44 $\qquad$ $\frac{1}{2}$ of 20

11. $\frac{1}{4}$ of 20 $\qquad$ $\frac{1}{2}$ of 10 $\qquad$ $\frac{1}{3}$ of 6

12. 6 cars were parked in front of the church. Seven times as many were parked behind the church. How many cars were parked behind the church?

13. The zoo had an elephant that was 65 years old. A bear was 47 years old. How much younger was the bear than the elephant?

155

1. $3\overline{)8}$ $4\overline{)39}$ $4\overline{)11}$ $3\overline{)11}$

2. $4\overline{)31}$ $4\overline{)10}$ $4\overline{)38}$ $4\overline{)27}$

3. $4\overline{)30}$ $4\overline{)19}$ $4\overline{)35}$ $4\overline{)26}$

4. $3\overline{)7}$ $4\overline{)34}$ $4\overline{)18}$ $3\overline{)10}$

5. $\begin{array}{r} 9 \\ \times 9 \\ \hline \end{array}$ $\begin{array}{r} 7 \\ \times 9 \\ \hline \end{array}$ $\begin{array}{r} 9 \\ \times 6 \\ \hline \end{array}$ $\begin{array}{r} 8 \\ \times 9 \\ \hline \end{array}$ $\begin{array}{r} 4 \\ \times 6 \\ \hline \end{array}$ $\begin{array}{r} 12 \\ \times 7 \\ \hline \end{array}$ $\begin{array}{r} 9 \\ \times 7 \\ \hline \end{array}$

6. $\begin{array}{r} 12 \\ \times 3 \\ \hline \end{array}$ $\begin{array}{r} 6 \\ \times 8 \\ \hline \end{array}$ $\begin{array}{r} 7 \\ \times 6 \\ \hline \end{array}$ $\begin{array}{r} 3 \\ \times 9 \\ \hline \end{array}$ $\begin{array}{r} 5 \\ \times 9 \\ \hline \end{array}$ $\begin{array}{r} 4 \\ \times 9 \\ \hline \end{array}$ $\begin{array}{r} 2 \\ \times 9 \\ \hline \end{array}$

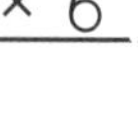

"Praise the LORD . . . all deeps." Psalm 148:7

7. $8 \times 8 + 2 =$ $7 \times 8 + 3 =$

8. $4 \times 8 + 2 =$ $8 \times 5 + 3 =$

9. $8 \times 7 + 3 =$ $6 \times 10 + 2 =$

10. $5 \times 5 + 2 =$ $7 \times 10 + 2 =$

11. eight thousand, three hundred seventy-five

12. seven thousand, ninety-six

13. nine thousand, four hundred forty-nine

14. six thousand, nine hundred seven

15. five thousand, seven hundred thirty-eight

16.

349	507	787	736	677
− 82	− 339	+ 46	− 498	+ 593

17.

945	465	609	889	838
− 677	+ 369	− 440	+ 382	− 599

1. $4\overline{)39}$ $4\overline{)31}$ $4\overline{)35}$ $3\overline{)28}$

2. $4\overline{)34}$ $3\overline{)23}$ $4\overline{)38}$ $3\overline{)20}$

3. $4\overline{)23}$ $3\overline{)17}$ $4\overline{)21}$ $4\overline{)18}$

4. $4\overline{)37}$ $4\overline{)26}$ $3\overline{)14}$ $2\overline{)19}$

5.

12	7	8	5	7	6	8
× 8	× 9	× 9	× 9	× 8	× 9	× 8

6.

9	12	8	9	9	9	9
× 7	× 9	× 7	× 5	× 8	× 9	× 6

"He cutteth out rivers among the rocks." Job 28:10

Write the Roman numerals.

7. 5 17 15 19

8. 16 10 18 20

9. 10 dimes + 10 nickels

4 quarters + 5 nickels

10. 2 half dollars + 9 nickels

2 quarters + 12 nickels

11. 1 half dollar + 1 quarter

3 quarters + 8 dimes

12. Father bought 1 pound of nails for his woodworking shop. How many ounces was that? *Write the rule.*

13. Mother got 1 pint of blueberries from the freezer to make a pie. How many cups was that? *Write the rule.*

1. 4)26   3)23   4)18   4)27

2. 4)10   4)17   2)15   4)11

3. 4)14   4)39   4)34   4)15

4. 3)14   2)17   3)29   4)19

5.

9	8	6	8	7	7	12
× 9	× 9	× 9	× 7	× 6	× 9	× 9

6.

8	9	6	7	9	9	12
× 8	× 7	× 7	× 8	× 6	× 8	× 8

"He cutteth out rivers among the rocks." Job 28:10

7.

8.

9. $\frac{1}{4}$ of 36 $\frac{1}{3}$ of 21 $\frac{1}{2}$ of 12

10. $\frac{1}{2}$ of 24 $\frac{1}{4}$ of 12 $\frac{1}{4}$ of 32

11. $\frac{1}{3}$ of 24 $\frac{1}{2}$ of 6 $\frac{1}{4}$ of 48

12. $\frac{1}{3}$ of 18 $\frac{1}{4}$ of 28 $\frac{1}{3}$ of 27

13. Jay saved money for 1 year to buy a Bible. How many months was that? *Write the rule.*

14. Mother set 1 quart of juice on the breakfast table. How many pints was that? *Write the rule.*

158

1. $4\overline{)35}$ $4\overline{)26}$ $4\overline{)39}$ $4\overline{)22}$

2. $2\overline{)13}$ $4\overline{)34}$ $3\overline{)16}$ $4\overline{)38}$

3. $4\overline{)31}$ $4\overline{)19}$ $4\overline{)14}$ $4\overline{)11}$

4. $4\overline{)18}$ $3\overline{)23}$ $4\overline{)10}$ $2\overline{)7}$

5. 8×8 12×9 9×7 8×9 6×9 7×8 12×8

6. 12×7 7×7 8×7 9×6 9×8 7×9 9×9

"He cutteth out rivers among the rocks." Job 28:10

7.

705	787	984	778	867
$-$ 436	+ 668	$-$ 396	+ 98	$-$ 789

8.

334	940	633	675	659
$-$ 257	$-$ 65	$-$ 46	+ 779	$-$ 391

9. $9 \times 7 + 2 =$ $\qquad$ $8 \times 7 + 1 =$

10. $9 \times 8 + 3 =$ $\qquad$ $9 \times 6 + 2 =$

11. $9 \times 9 + 3 =$ $\qquad$ $9 \times 5 + 3 =$

12. Henry has 24 hens. $\frac{1}{2}$ of them are brown. How many hens are brown?

13. Father helped to plant 12 trees in the church parking lot. $\frac{1}{3}$ of them were oak. How many trees were oak?

14. Mother had 32 tulips in bloom. She picked $\frac{1}{4}$ of them for a friend in the hospital. How many tulips did she pick?

1.

12	9	7	8	8	6	12
× 9	× 6	× 7	× 6	× 8	× 9	× 8

2.

8	8	12	9	5	7	9
× 9	× 7	× 6	× 9	× 9	× 6	× 7

3.

9	9	8	6	7	6	7
× 8	× 6	× 8	× 8	× 7	× 9	× 9

4.

12	6	9	9	8	7	12
× 8	× 7	× 5	× 9	× 9	× 8	× 9

5.

73	96	84	74	93	49
× 9	× 5	× 8	× 6	× 8	× 4

6.

72	84	72	83	94	63
× 8	× 9	× 7	× 7	× 7	× 8

7.

64	45	92	63	93	49
× 9	× 5	× 9	× 5	× 6	× 3

"He sendeth the springs into the valleys." Psalm 104:10

8.

777	981	965	404	963
- 448	- 506	- 685	- 76	- 489

9.

1 half dollar	2 quarters
+ 3 quarters	+ 7 nickels

10.

2 half dollars	10 dimes
+ 11 nickels	+ 1 quarter

11.

4 quarters	9 nickels
+ 5 nickels	+ 79 pennies

12. 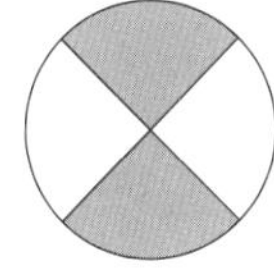  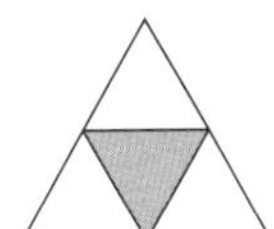 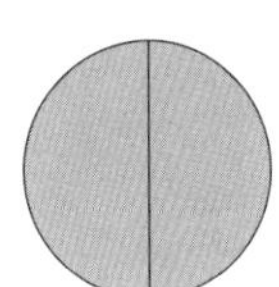

13. Fred's family sat under a tree and shelled peas. Fred shelled 4 cups. How many quarts of peas was that? *Write the rule.*

14. Mother made 1 quart of bean soup for lunch. How many cups was that? *Write the rule.*

1.	8 × 9	8 × 7	5 × 9	9 × 9	6 × 6	12 × 8	8 × 6
2.	9 × 7	9 × 5	7 × 8	12 × 8	4 × 9	9 × 9	9 × 8
3.	12 × 6	8 × 8	5 × 8	12 × 9	7 × 9	6 × 9	6 × 8
4.	7 × 9	12 × 9	8 × 5	8 × 8	9 × 6	9 × 7	8 × 9

5.	90 × 9	73 × 9	91 × 2	94 × 8	84 × 7	31 × 9
6.	86 × 5	63 × 3	81 × 9	35 × 5	81 × 8	50 × 9
7.	64 × 9	92 × 3	72 × 8	95 × 7	80 × 7	94 × 7

"He sendeth the springs into the valleys." Psalm 104:10

Write the Roman numerals.

8. 9 6 12 14

9. 4 11 7 13

10.

$9.83	$6.70	$3.75	$9.91
- 3.56	+ .99	+ 3.59	- 1.48

11.

$9.90	$7.82	$2.63	$2.82
- 2.22	- .49	+ 5.79	+ 3.44

12. At the bookstore Carl bought a Bible bookmark for $1.68 and a pencil for $1.98. What sum of money was that?

13. Father treated the family to 9 ice cream cones. $\frac{1}{3}$ of them were cherry. How many cones were cherry?

14. Sixteen shirts flapped on the clothesline. $\frac{1}{4}$ of them were blue. How many shirts were blue?

1. 9×7 8×6 9×4 7×6 12×8 6×4 9×9

2. 12×7 12×3 6×8 12×8 6×7 3×8 6×9

3. 7×9 8×9 12×9 4×4 7×7 8×7 9×9

4. 12×7 7×8 7×7 2×8 12×9 9×8 9×6

5. 704×9 862×4 803×8 423×3 710×8

6. 602×7 803×9 851×7 912×5 903×9

7. 732×3 943×2 813×6 641×9 761×6

"He sendeth the springs into the valleys." Psalm 104:10

8.  

9.   

10. six thousand, four hundred eighty

11. eight thousand, two hundred six

12. nine thousand, fifty-nine

13. In the Bible, King Solomon's throne had 2 lions on each step. There were $\frac{1}{2}$ dozen steps. How many lions was that in all?

14. Aunt Ruth is 101 years old, and Mae is nine. How much younger is Mae than Aunt Ruth?

15. Father planted seven trees along the lane. He planted 9 times as many in the orchard. How many trees did he plant in the orchard?

1.	9)63	8)56	6)24	4)36	8)72
2.	8)40	5)45	5)20	7)49	8)48
3.	8)48	6)54	8)16	5)45	7)42
4.	9)45	9)72	7)21	5)35	9)54
5.	8)56	4)28	6)18	8)64	9)81

6.	4)80	2)46	3)36	4)88	3)96
7.	4)84	3)39	2)60	2)26	3)63
8.	3)69	3)60	3)66	4)48	2)64
9.	3)99	3)93	2)24	3)90	2)66

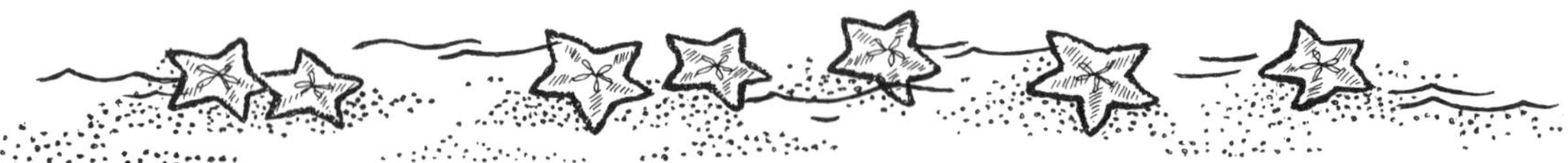

"I will declare thy greatness." Psalm 145:6

10.

45	74	53	43	72	74
22	25	25	25	6	13
+ 97	+ 80	+ 47	+ 63	+ 69	+ 69

11.

82	56	63	53	32	34
36	23	4	24	45	42
+ 6	+ 99	+ 96	+ 78	+ 69	+ 54

12. 7 + 9 − 8 =   16 − 9 + 6 =

13. 15 − 7 + 4 =   8 + 6 − 7 =

14. 12 − 3 + 7 =   7 + 6 − 8 =

15. 18 − 9 + 7 =   17 − 8 + 6 =

16. Wilmer's little brother helped to hoe the garden. His hoe was 1 yard long. How many inches was that? *Write the rule.*

17. Jane watered her pepper plants with 1 quart of water. How many cups was that? *Write the rule.*

1.	$9\overline{)54}$	$7\overline{)63}$	$8\overline{)32}$	$8\overline{)16}$	$8\overline{)56}$
2.	$7\overline{)56}$	$7\overline{)28}$	$6\overline{)54}$	$9\overline{)63}$	$9\overline{)18}$
3.	$7\overline{)49}$	$9\overline{)72}$	$9\overline{)9}$	$8\overline{)64}$	$6\overline{)42}$
4.	$6\overline{)48}$	$8\overline{)40}$	$4\overline{)16}$	$4\overline{)28}$	$8\overline{)72}$
5.	$8\overline{)48}$	$9\overline{)36}$	$9\overline{)45}$	$9\overline{)81}$	$3\overline{)21}$

6.	$8\overline{)568}$	$9\overline{)630}$	$4\overline{)328}$	$5\overline{)305}$
7.	$6\overline{)420}$	$6\overline{)546}$	$8\overline{)640}$	$3\overline{)246}$
8.	$9\overline{)729}$	$5\overline{)400}$	$4\overline{)364}$	$9\overline{)810}$
9.	$9\overline{)549}$	$7\overline{)567}$	$8\overline{)720}$	$7\overline{)497}$

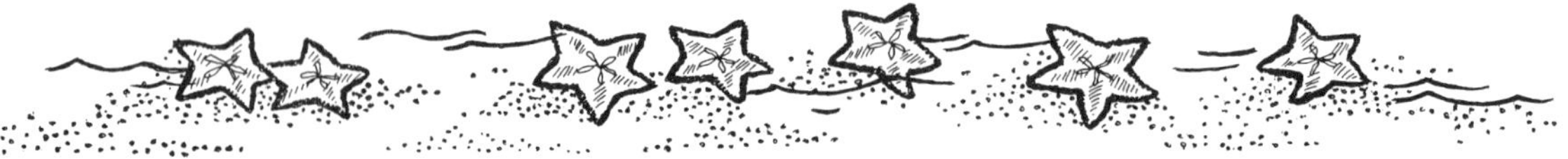

"I will declare thy greatness." Psalm 145:6

10. 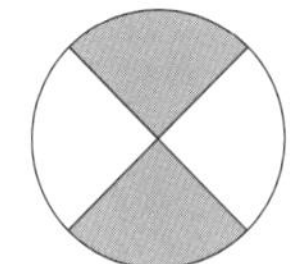 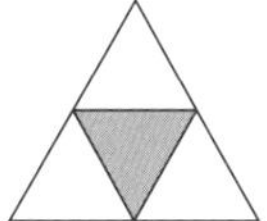 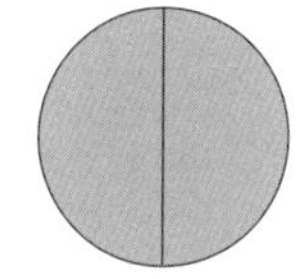

11. 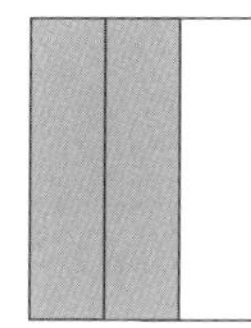 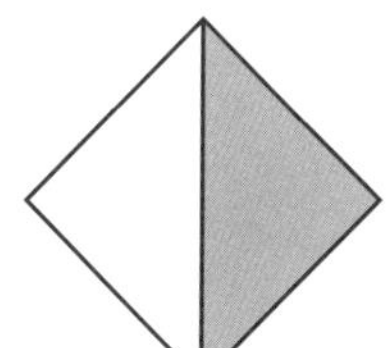 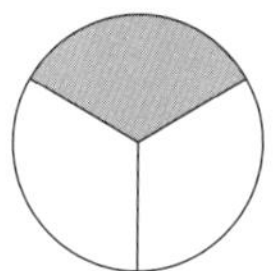 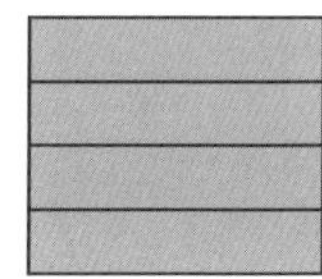

12. $81 \div 9 =$ $36 \div 9 =$ $56 \div 8 =$

13. $64 \div 8 =$ $63 \div 7 =$ $96 \div 8 =$

14. $108 \div 9 =$ $45 \div 5 =$ $72 \div 9 =$

15. $63 \div 9 =$ $32 \div 8 =$ $72 \div 8 =$

16. $48 \div 8 =$ $84 \div 7 =$ $30 \div 5 =$

17. Susan fed her pet lambs 1 quart of milk. How many cups was that? *Write the rule.*

18. In the Bible, $\frac{1}{2}$ dozen covered wagons were given as a gift for the Lord's work. How many wagons was that? *Write the rule.*

1.	$4\overline{)39}$	$4\overline{)34}$	$4\overline{)15}$	$4\overline{)31}$
2.	$3\overline{)14}$	$4\overline{)10}$	$4\overline{)38}$	$3\overline{)17}$
3.	$3\overline{)29}$	$3\overline{)25}$	$4\overline{)14}$	$4\overline{)30}$
4.	$4\overline{)17}$	$2\overline{)5}$	$4\overline{)37}$	$3\overline{)16}$

5.	$9\overline{)963}$	$4\overline{)836}$	$7\overline{)763}$	$9\overline{)972}$
6.	$8\overline{)872}$	$8\overline{)856}$	$8\overline{)864}$	$3\overline{)627}$

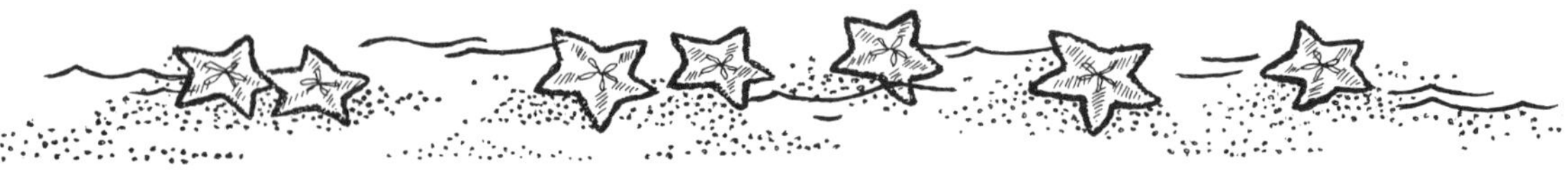

"I will declare thy greatness." Psalm 145:6

Write the Roman numerals.

7. 20   14   15   17

8. 13   19   18   16

9.

489	485	472	666	972
+ 758	− 99	+ 889	− 578	− 568

10.

584	727	550	904	713
+ 776	− 540	+ 696	− 519	− 269

11. Roy taught his little sister 23 songs from *Silver Gems* and 5 songs from *Life Songs.* He has 1 dozen other songs he wants to teach her. How many songs is that altogether?

12. Fifteen sparrows sat in a tree. $\frac{1}{3}$ of them sang. How many sparrow sang?

13. There are 20 windows in the church house. Rose cleaned $\frac{1}{4}$ of them. How many windows did Rose clean?

1.	7 × 9	7 × 8	4 × 8	9 × 9	6 × 6	8 × 5	8 × 9
2.	12 × 8	9 × 9	8 × 4	8 × 7	5 × 8	4 × 9	12 × 7
3.	9 × 7	5 × 9	4 × 6	6 × 9	8 × 6	8 × 8	9 × 8
4.	12 × 9	12 × 2	9 × 5	8 × 8	6 × 8	9 × 6	12 × 6

5.	94 × 8	39 × 3	92 × 9	84 × 8	75 × 6	74 × 9
6.	97 × 4	53 × 8	54 × 9	45 × 4	34 × 9	74 × 8
7.	62 × 9	74 × 8	93 × 7	65 × 6	63 × 8	84 × 9

"Thy thoughts . . . O God! . . . are more in number than the sand." Psalm 139:17, 18

8. 

9.   

10.

2 quarters + 10 nickels	7 dollars + 4 quarters

11.

9 nickels + 89 pennies	3 quarters + 13 nickels

12.

1 half dollar + 1 quarter	2 half dollars + 10 dimes

13. Lester poured 4 quarts of water into his fish bowl. How many gallons was that? *Write the rule.*

14. When Fay's family ate a picnic lunch by the meadow brook, they drank 1 gallon of mint tea. How many quarts was that? *Write the rule.*

1. 12×9 $\quad 5 \times 9$ $\quad 7 \times 8$ $\quad 8 \times 8$ $\quad 8 \times 7$ $\quad 9 \times 5$ $\quad 12 \times 7$

2. 7×9 $\quad 9 \times 6$ $\quad 9 \times 9$ $\quad 6 \times 8$ $\quad 4 \times 8$ $\quad 8 \times 9$ $\quad 3 \times 9$

3. 6×9 $\quad 9 \times 7$ $\quad 8 \times 4$ $\quad 8 \times 6$ $\quad 9 \times 9$ $\quad 9 \times 3$ $\quad 9 \times 8$

4. 12×6 $\quad 6 \times 9$ $\quad 9 \times 7$ $\quad 7 \times 7$ $\quad 7 \times 9$ $\quad 9 \times 6$ $\quad 12 \times 8$

---

5. 92×9 $\quad 83 \times 7$ $\quad 90 \times 8$ $\quad 95 \times 5$ $\quad 94 \times 7$ $\quad 51 \times 9$

6. 54×8 $\quad 64 \times 9$ $\quad 71 \times 7$ $\quad 83 \times 9$ $\quad 60 \times 7$ $\quad 81 \times 8$

7. 83×6 $\quad 32 \times 9$ $\quad 70 \times 8$ $\quad 93 \times 6$ $\quad 63 \times 8$ $\quad 70 \times 9$

"Thy thoughts . . . O God! . . . are more in number than the sand." Psalm 139:17, 18

8.

443	968	764	702	558
+ 976	- 673	+ 798	- 454	- 77

9.

873	749	772	867	330
- 579	+ 669	+ 789	- 387	- 83

10. 14 - 5 + 8 = 13 - 6 + 9 =

11. 15 - 6 + 9 = 17 - 8 + 7 =

12. 14 - 8 + 7 = 17 - 9 + 5 =

13. 13 - 8 + 9 = 11 - 6 + 8 =

14. Mother sewed 8 buttons on each shirt. She made 9 shirts. How many buttons was that altogether?

15. Mae picked 137 buttercups. She put 78 of them in a jar on the table. She pressed the rest. How many buttercups did she press?

16. A mighty wave traveled 40 miles each hour for 9 hours. How many miles did it travel in all?

	a	b	c	d	e	f	g
1.	12 × 9	9 × 9	6 × 9	8 × 4	4 × 8	9 × 6	9 × 9
2.	12 × 7	8 × 9	7 × 8	12 × 3	6 × 6	8 × 7	9 × 8
3.	7 × 9	9 × 4	7 × 9	12 × 4	5 × 9	7 × 5	12 × 8
4.	4 × 9	9 × 7	6 × 8	9 × 7	5 × 7	9 × 5	12 × 6

	a	b	c	d	e
5.	802 × 9	831 × 7	903 × 8	713 × 7	720 × 9
6.	902 × 5	716 × 6	604 × 8	983 × 3	812 × 8
7.	603 × 9	902 × 7	504 × 9	814 × 6	704 × 8

"Thy thoughts . . . O God! . . . are more in number than the sand." Psalm 139:17, 18

8. 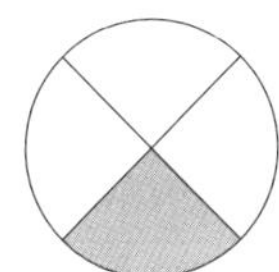 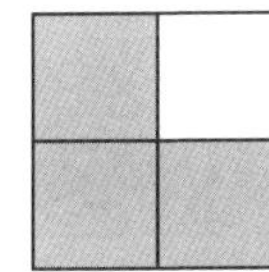 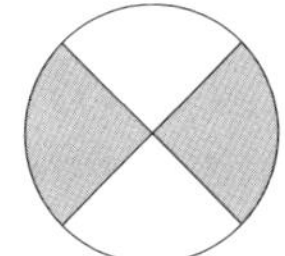 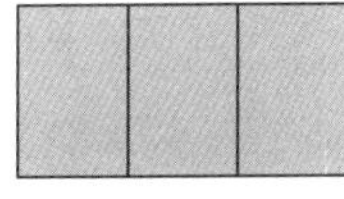

9. 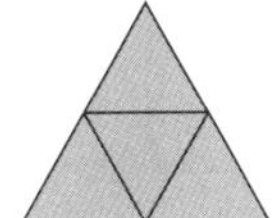 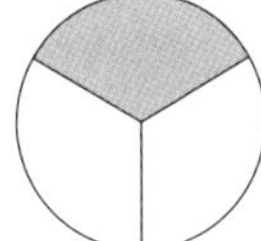 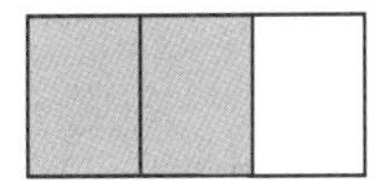 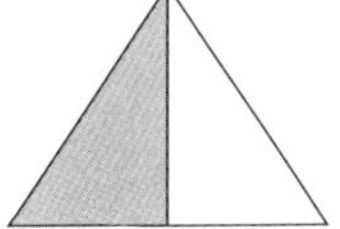

10. $72 \div 8 =$ $\quad 24 \div 6 =$ $\quad 63 \div 9 =$

11. $56 \div 8 =$ $\quad 40 \div 8 =$ $\quad 81 \div 9 =$

12. $54 \div 6 =$ $\quad 54 \div 9 =$ $\quad 36 \div 4 =$

13. God made the earth in 6 days. He made the animals on $\frac{1}{3}$ of those days. In how many days did God make the animals?

14. A wave swept 48 shells up on the sand. Roy's family picked up $\frac{1}{4}$ of them. How many shell did they pick up?

15. The children in Lee's classroom sailed leaf boats in the brook. One dozen boats were green. $\frac{1}{2}$ dozen were brown. 9 were red. What sum of boats was that?

1. 9)108 9)63 7)84 7)49 8)96

2. 8)64 7)42 9)81 4)28 7)56

3. 6)36 4)32 6)48 8)56 8)72

4. 5)45 7)14 3)12 6)54 3)18

5. 4)16 5)10 3)27 5)30 7)63

---

6. 4)80 2)46 2)64 3)93 3)66

7. 3)69 4)84 2)60 3)39 2)86

8. 4)88 2)62 3)96 3)69 3)60

9. 2)84 2)26 3)90 3)63 2)46

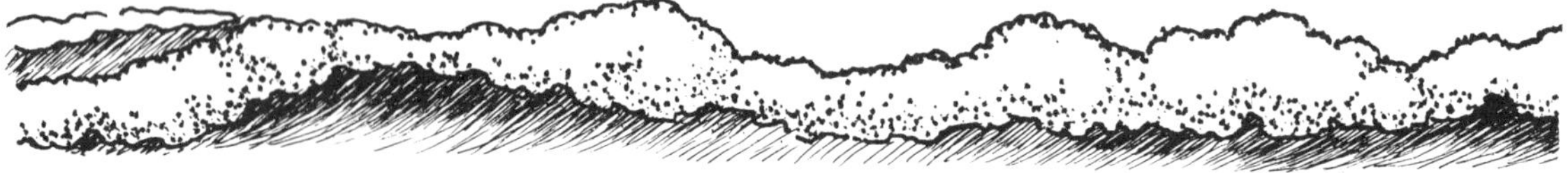

"The sea is his." Psalm 95:5

Write the Roman numerals.

10. 6 15 20 10

11. 9 19 16 7

12. $\frac{1}{3}$ of 27 $\frac{1}{2}$ of 16 $\frac{1}{3}$ of 21

13. $\frac{1}{4}$ of 36 $\frac{1}{4}$ of 28 $\frac{1}{4}$ of 32

14. $\frac{1}{3}$ of 9 $\frac{1}{4}$ of 24 $\frac{1}{2}$ of 18

15. $\begin{array}{r} 859 \\ -\ 487 \\ \hline \end{array}$ $\begin{array}{r} 984 \\ -\ 689 \\ \hline \end{array}$ $\begin{array}{r} 902 \\ -\ 275 \\ \hline \end{array}$ $\begin{array}{r} 363 \\ -\ 69 \\ \hline \end{array}$ $\begin{array}{r} 934 \\ -\ 308 \\ \hline \end{array}$

16. Before Glen cut the grass, he put 1 gallon of gas in the mower. How many quarts was that? *Write the rule.*

17. Ann heard waves splashing every day for 1 year when her family lived by the sea to help with a church. How many days was that? *Write the rule.*

1.	9)72	6)42	9)36	6)72	7)84
2.	7)42	5)60	7)28	7)49	9)81
3.	8)48	7)56	9)108	6)48	9)54
4.	6)36	6)54	8)56	9)45	8)72
5.	8)64	5)25	9)63	7)63	8)96

6.	9)639	3)159	8)560	5)405
7.	2)106	4)368	5)205	6)420
8.	9)450	6)246	3)276	9)810
9.	6)486	7)350	8)720	7)497

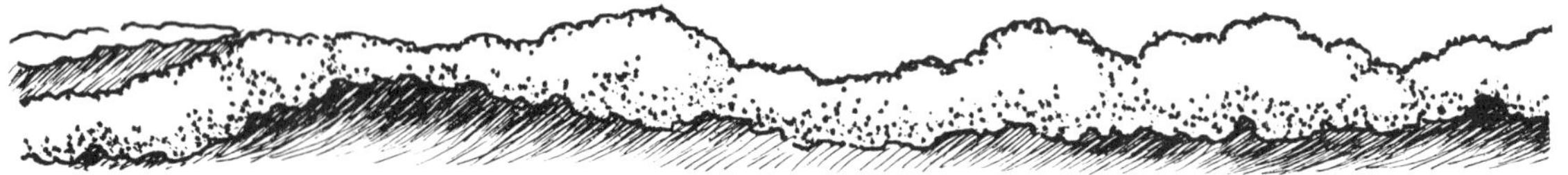

"The sea is his." Psalm 95:5

10. 

11.   

12.

$9.85	$7.79	$9.94	$3.97
- 3.39	+ .97	- 5.25	+ 2.60

13.

$4.68	$7.96	$9.84	$8.93
+ 1.88	- 3.28	- 1.09	- 2.48

14. 1 gallon of sap dripped from a maple tree into a bucket. How many quarts was that? *Write the rule.*

15. Keith dipped 1 quart of water from the Atlantic Ocean and took it home to show to his classmates. How many cups was that? *Write the rule.*

1. $4\overline{)38}$ $4\overline{)34}$ $4\overline{)35}$ $4\overline{)30}$

2. $4\overline{)33}$ $3\overline{)28}$ $2\overline{)15}$ $3\overline{)26}$

3. $4\overline{)26}$ $4\overline{)31}$ $4\overline{)39}$ $4\overline{)27}$

4. $3\overline{)23}$ $3\overline{)19}$ $3\overline{)20}$ $3\overline{)29}$

5. $9\overline{)963}$ $5\overline{)540}$ $4\overline{)836}$ $9\overline{)972}$

6. $3\overline{)627}$ $7\overline{)756}$ $8\overline{)856}$ $8\overline{)864}$

7. $\begin{array}{r} 4 \text{ quarters} \\ + 2 \text{ half dollars} \\ \hline \end{array}$ $\begin{array}{r} 3 \text{ quarters} \\ + 11 \text{ nickels} \\ \hline \end{array}$

8. $\begin{array}{r} 1 \text{ half dollar} \\ + 7 \text{ nickels} \\ \hline \end{array}$ $\begin{array}{r} 7 \text{ dimes} \\ + 5 \text{ nickels} \\ \hline \end{array}$

9. $9 \times 7 + 3 =$ $8 \times 12 + 3 =$

10. $7 \times 8 + 2 =$ $9 \times 6 + 3 =$

11. $9 \times 11 + 1 =$ $8 \times 8 + 1 =$

12. $7 \times 12 + 1 =$ $9 \times 9 + 3 =$

13. $7 \times 7 + 1 =$

"The LORD on high is mightier than . . .
the mighty waves of the sea."

Psalm 93:4

INDEX

Bold numbers are lesson numbers of first use.